Revise
AS Physics

Pauline Anning
Bernard Taylor
Elizabeth Swinbank

Heinemann
Inspiring generations

Heinemann Educational Publishers
Halley Court, Jordan Hill, Oxford OX2 8EJ
Part of Harcourt Education

Heinemann is the registered trademark of
Harcourt Education Limited

© Pauline Anning, Bernard Taylor, University of York Science Education Group 2004

First published 2004

08 07 06
10 9 8 7 6 5 4 3 2

British Library Cataloguing in Publication Data is available
from the British Library on request.

10-digit ISBN: 0 435583 45 X
13-digit ISBN: 978 0 435583 45 3

Edited by Anne Trevillion
Index compiled by Paul Nash

Designed and typeset by Saxon Graphics Ltd, Derby

Original illustrations © Harcourt Education Limited 2004

Printed and bound in Great Britain by Thomson Litho Ltd, Glasgow

Acknowledgements

The examination questions are reproduced by kind permission of London Qualifications Ltd,
trading as Edexcel. The worked exam questions in the text are taken from the following
papers:

Unit PSA1
Page 10: June 2000; page 17: January 2000; page 19: June 2000; page 22: January 1999.

Unit PSA2
Page 38: June 2000; page 40: January 2000; page 42: January 2001; page 44: June 2001;
page 47: January 2001; page 49: June 2001; page 54: January 2000; page 56: June 2000;
page 59: June 2001; page 64: June 1999.

The practice exam questions on pages 30–34 and 68–73 are taken from the papers specified
at the end of each question.

Note: London Qualifications Ltd accepts no responsibility whatsoever for the accuracy or
method of working in the answers given.

Every effort has been made to contact copyright holders of material reproduced in this book.
Any omissions will be rectified in subsequent printings if notice is given to the publishers.

Contents

Introduction – How to revise

This revision guide is written to help you prepare for the AS exams for the Salters Horners Advanced Physics (SHAP) course. The syllabus is Edexcel Physics (Salters Horners).

In the SHAP course, you study physics within a variety of contexts and applications. The exams will test your knowledge and understanding of the physics concepts and principles, *not* the contexts in which you studied them. The exam questions will ask you to apply this knowledge to particular situations. Some of these might be familiar to you from the course, but many will be unfamiliar.

The SHAP course is designed so that you will meet most key physics concepts several times, gradually building up your experience. Some concepts are introduced in one assessment unit but not tested until later. For example, refractive index is introduced in The Sound of Music in Unit PSA1 but not tested until you meet it again in Good Enough to Eat in Unit PSA2.

This book summarises the 'bare bones' of the physics content of the course, stripped away from the contexts in which you learned it. This is the content on which examiners can set questions. It is listed in the syllabus specification as 'Learning outcomes' and in your textbook as 'Achievements'.

The **content summary** includes some equations, as these are a convenient way to express many things in physics. **Boxed equations** need to be learned. Others are either given to you at the back of the exam paper or can be derived from those memorised or given. However, equations are *not* the most important aspect of physics.

When revising, try to make sure you understand the topic. If you are unsure of anything, go back to your textbook or ask your teacher for help. Questions and activities at the end of each chapter provide activities to help you, for example making summary charts and mind maps. Ask your teacher and discuss the ideas with other students who are revising the same topic. Talking about ideas and explaining them to yourself and to other people really does help you to make sense of them and fix them in your mind.

At the start of each unit in this revision guide there is a short **introduction** which tells you what is covered by that unit.

Within each unit the content is divided into short spreads of one to four pages, which each revise a section or sections of your textbook. The spreads end with **quick check questions** to help you test your understanding. Try to do them before consulting the **answers** towards the back of the book.

You will find **practice exam questions** from past papers at the end of each unit. Try these only when you are fairly confident that you have revised a unit thoroughly. The outline **answers** at the back of the book indicate points that examiners award marks for. These are *not* model answers!

When answering exam questions, always be careful with details such as units, and using a sharp pencil for graphs. Not doing these could easily lose you marks. Some questions ask you to 'explain' or 'describe' something. This can be more difficult than doing a calculation. Read your answers through afterwards to see if they make sense to someone who does not already know the answer. The **worked examples** and **worked exam questions** in the text are designed to show you the sorts of things the examiners look for.

Unit PSA1: Physics at Work, Rest and Play

This unit tests:

- **High, Faster, Stronger (HFS)**
- **Technology in Space (SPC)**
- **The Sound of Music (MUS)**

This part of the revision guide follows the same order as your AS textbook. The heading of each spread indicates the physics content covered and there is a reference to the relevant section(s) of your textbook where you will find further details.

Motion equations and graphs
HFS Sections 1.2 and 1.3

- **Scalar** quantities have only magnitude (size), e.g. a speed of 3 m s^{-1}, or a distance of 6 m.
- **Vector** quantities have size and direction, e.g. a velocity of 2 m s^{-1} to the north, or a displacement along the *x*-axis. For motion back and forth along a straight line, vector quantities are represented by their magnitudes and direction is indicated by positive and negative signs.

Equations of motion

$$v = \frac{\Delta x}{\Delta t} \quad \text{or} \quad v = \frac{\Delta s}{\Delta t}$$

$$a = \frac{(v - u)}{t} = \frac{\Delta v}{\Delta t} \quad (\text{or} \quad v = u + at)$$

where *x* or *s* is **displacement** (m), *t* is time (s), *v* and *u* are **velocity** (m s^{-1}) and *a* is **acceleration** (m s^{-2}).

For motion with constant acceleration:

$$v^2 = u^2 + 2as$$

$$s = ut + \tfrac{1}{2}at^2$$

A *negative acceleration* means that *speed in the positive direction is decreasing*, or that *speed in the negative direction is increasing*.

An object in *free fall* is influenced only by gravity. Near the Earth's surface it has constant acceleration *g* = 9.81 m s^{-2} vertically downwards.

- You will be expected to remember these relationships.
- The delta symbol, Δ, means 'the change in', 'the difference in' or 'a small amount of'.

✓ *Quick check 1*

Worked example

A student used a toy bow and arrow to fire the arrow 4.0 m vertically into the air. Neglecting air resistance, what was the arrow's initial velocity? How long did it take for the arrow to reach 4.0 m?

Step 1 Write down what you know, and what you want to know:

$$s = 4.0 \text{ m}, u = ?, v = 0.0 \text{ m s}^{-1}, a = -9.81 \text{ m s}^{-2}, t = ?$$

Step 2 Rearrange the appropriate equation and substitute values to find *u*:

$$v^2 = u^2 + 2as \quad \text{so} \quad u^2 = v^2 - 2as$$

$$u^2 = 0 - (2 \times -9.81 \text{ m s}^{-2} \times 4.0 \text{ m}) = 78.5 \text{ m}^2 \text{ s}^{-2}$$

$$u = \sqrt{78.5} \text{ m s}^{-1} = 8.9 \text{ m s}^{-1}$$

Step 3 Calculate *t*:

$$v = u + at \quad \text{so} \quad t = \frac{(v - u)}{a} = \frac{(0 - 8.9 \text{m s}^{-1})}{-9.81 \text{m s}^{-2}} = 0.91 \text{ s}$$

- Take care with signs. If upwards is taken to be positive, then acceleration due to gravity is negative.
- Make sure your answer has the correct units.

✓ *Quick check 2, 3*

Graphical representations

- Velocity is equal to the *gradient of a displacement–time graph*.

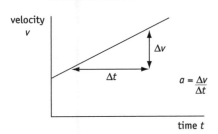
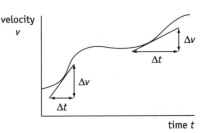

- Acceleration is equal to the *gradient of a velocity–time graph*.

- Displacement is equal to the *area under a velocity–time graph*.

Worked example

The figure shows the motion of a cyclist. What was her acceleration 6 s after starting from rest? How far did she travel in those 6 s?

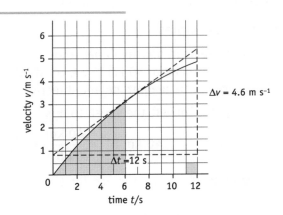

Step 1   From the gradient of the tangent, acceleration

$$a = \frac{\Delta v}{\Delta t} = \frac{4.6\,\text{m s}^{-1}}{12\,\text{s}} = 0.38 \text{ m s}^{-2}.$$

Step 2   The area of the shaded square represents 0.5 m. There are about 20 such squares under the graph, so the distance travelled is about 10 m.

▶ Draw a large triangle and read the values from the axes.

✓ *Quick check 4*

Quick check questions

1   Rearrange the expression $v = u + at$ to make t the subject.

2   A coin is dropped down a well and strikes the bottom after 2.0 s. How deep is the well?

3   A cyclist accelerates from rest to 5.0 m s^{-1} over a distance of 30 m. What is his acceleration?

4   Describe in words how the acceleration of the cyclist in the Worked example changes during the time shown. What is her initial acceleration?

Force and acceleration
HFS Section 1.4

Acceleration is always caused by **force**. The direction of the acceleration is always the same as that of the net force that produces it.

If there is *no* force acting on an object, or two or more forces exactly balance one another, then the object continues to move at constant speed in a straight line, or remains at rest.

If there is an *unbalanced force* on an object, its velocity changes. The acceleration *a* is related to the net force, *F*:

$$F = ma = \frac{m\Delta v}{\Delta t}$$

where *m* is the object's mass.

Forces between two objects

Forces always arise from an interaction between two objects. The two objects exert forces on one another of equal magnitude but in opposite directions.

Worked examples

1   A four-person bobsleigh has a total mass of 630 kg. The bobsleigh finishes its run at a speed of 40 km h^{-1}. A constant braking force brings it to rest in 9 s. What are the magnitude and direction of the braking force?

   Step 1   Convert the speed to m s^{-1}:

   $$40 \text{ km h}^{-1} = \frac{40 \text{ km}}{1 \text{ h}} = \frac{40 \times 10^{3} \text{ m}}{3600 \text{ s}} = 11.1 \text{ m s}^{-1}$$

   > When converting units, set out your calculation clearly so that you can keep track of what you are doing.

   Step 2   Calculate the acceleration *a*:

   $$v = u + at \quad \text{SO} \quad a = \frac{(v - u)}{t} = \frac{(0 - 11.1 \text{ m s}^{-1})}{9 \text{ s}} = -1.2 \text{ m s}^{-2}$$

   Step 3   Calculate the force *F*:

   $$F = ma = 630 \text{ kg} \times -1.2 \text{ m s}^{-2} = -756 \text{ N}$$

   The negative sign shows that the force acts in the opposite direction to the sleigh's motion.

2   A skydiver in free fall accelerates at 9.81 m s^{-2}. Which two objects are interacting to produce the force that causes his acceleration? Explain why both do *not* have the same acceleration.

   The interaction is between the skydiver and the Earth. The mass of the Earth is very much greater than the skydiver's, so the Earth's acceleration is very much smaller.

skydiver, mass 70 kg

gravitational force on person produces acceleration 9.8 m s^{-2}

Earth, mass 6 × 10^{24} kg

gravitational force on Earth produces negligible acceleration

Weight

Objects in free fall close to the Earth's surface always have the same acceleration, g, due to gravity. The gravitational force acting on an object is called its **weight**, W (with SI units of N):

$$W = mg$$

Gravitational field strength is the gravitational force acting on unit mass: $g = W/m$.

The SI units of gravitational field strength are newtons per kilogram, N kg^{-1}.

✓ *Quick check 1*

An object's **mass** does *not* depend on its location, but its **weight** on the Moon or elsewhere is different from its weight on Earth.

Worked example

On the Moon, the gravitational field strength is 1.6 N kg^{-1}. A container of Moon rocks weighed 500 N on the surface of the Moon. What do the samples weigh on Earth?

Step 1   Find the mass m. On the Moon, $W = mg_{Moon}$ so:

$$m = \frac{W}{g_{Moon}} = \frac{500 \text{ N}}{1.6 \text{ N kg}^{-1}} = 312.5 \text{ kg}$$

> ▶ Set out your reasoning so that it is clear what you are doing. Round your final answer to a sensible number of figures.

Step 2   Calculate the weight on Earth:

$$W = mg_{Earth} = 312.5 \text{ kg} \times 9.81 \text{ N kg}^{-1} = 3.1 \times 10^3 \text{ N}$$

✓ *Quick check 2–4*

❓ Quick check questions

1 State two equivalent versions of the SI units of g.

2 In each of the following situation, say whether there is, **A** no unbalanced force acting, **B** an unbalanced force acting in the direction of motion, or

   C an unbalanced force acting against the direction of motion.

   a A bottle of milk rests on a table.

   b A car starts to move off from a traffic light.

   c A cyclist travels at a constant speed heading due south.

   d A skydiver opens his parachute and his speed decreases.

   e A water drop rises vertically from a fountain.

   f A baby's soft toy comes to rest as it lands on the floor.

3 A 24.5 tonne aircraft lands on an aircraft carrier at a velocity of 252 km h^{-1} and is brought to rest over a distance of 70 m. Calculate the braking force. (Assume the force is constant.)

4 A firework rocket has a mass of 100 g and when lit gives a thrust of 1.50 N acting vertically upwards.

   a What is the weight of the rocket?

   b What unbalanced force acts on the rocket?

Combining and resolving forces
HFS Section 2.1

When two forces are acting on an object, the **resultant force** is found by adding the two force vectors. If two forces act along the same straight line, the resultant force is found by adding or subtracting their magnitudes.

Using a scale drawing

If there is an angle between the two forces, their resultant can be found by a *scale drawing*.

Worked example

One end of a spring is fixed at point A, and the other end is pulled to point B using two forcemeters as shown in the figure. What single force could replace these two forces? How could you modify the apparatus to check your result?

Make a scale drawing like that shown here. The resultant force acts along the direction AB and has magnitude 28.8 N. To check the answer, use a single forcemeter to extend the spring to B.

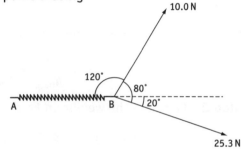

- *Choose a scale that is both simple and allows you to draw a large triangle, e.g. 1 cm to 1 N, or 1 cm to 5 N.*
- *Use a protractor to measure the angles.*
- *Use a sharp pencil and draw the lines carefully.*
- *Start the second vector from the tip of the first one.*
- *Remember to state the direction of the resultant force as well as its magnitude.*
- *It is hard to get a very precise result by drawing so a range of answers is acceptable, e.g. 28–30 N in this example.*

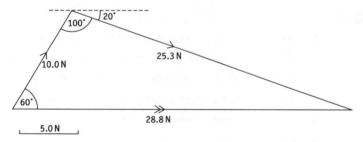

✓ Quick check 1

Forces at right angles

If the two forces are at right angles to each other, then the magnitude of the resultant can be found by Pythagoras and its direction using trigonometry. In the figure,

$$R^2 = F_1^2 + F_2^2$$

$$\tan \theta = \frac{F_1}{F_2}$$

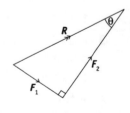

✓ Quick check 2

Resolving forces

Any single force can be treated as if it is made up of two forces acting *at right angles to each other*. Any force can be *resolved* into two *components* acting along, and at right angles to, any convenient direction.

If a force of magnitude F acts at an angle θ to a chosen direction, then:

- its component *along* that direction is $F \cos \theta$, and
- its component *at right angles* to that direction is $F \sin \theta$, which is the same as $F \cos (90° - \theta)$.

In **equilibrium**, that is, when there is no overall unbalanced force, the sum of the force components *in any direction* is zero.

Worked example

One climber is holding onto another to stop him falling. The two climbers have a combined weight of 1766 N. What is the tension in the rope?

Step 1 Resolve the tension T in each section of the rope:

vertical component = $T \cos 65°$, horizontal component = $T \sin 65°$

Step 2 Equate vertical components:

$$W = 2T \cos 65° \text{ so } T = \frac{W}{2 \cos 65°} = \frac{1766 \text{ N}}{2 \cos 65°} = 2089 \text{ N}$$

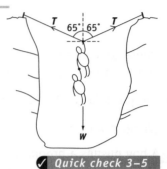

✓ *Quick check 3–5*

❓ Quick check questions

1 In the figure, what is the resultant force R?

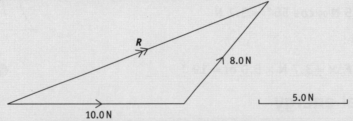

2 In the figure to the right showing forces acting at right angles, if $F_1 = 6.0$ N and $F_2 = 10.0$ N, what are R and θ?

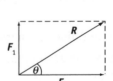

3 A force of magnitude $F = 75.0$ N acts at $\theta = 35°$ to the horizontal. What are its horizontal and vertical components?

4 A student pulls back the bowstring of a toy bow with a forcemeter and records 15.0 N. The angle between the strings is 110°. What is the tension in the string?

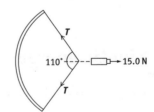

5 An architecture student assembles the apparatus shown to model the forces acting on part of a roof. The metre ruler rests firmly against base of the stand, with a reaction force acting outwards along the ruler. What is the tension in the string? What is the magnitude of the reaction force?

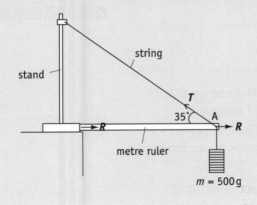

Energy, work and power
HFS Part 3

When a force causes motion it does **work**, and **energy** is transferred:

$$\Delta E = \Delta W = F\Delta x$$

where ΔE is the energy transferred, ΔW is the work done, Δx is the distance moved and F is the *component of the force along the direction of motion*.

The joule (J) is the SI unit of work and energy: 1 J = 1 N m.

Worked example

A boy pushes a broom with a force of 6.5 N acting along its handle at an angle of 55° to the floor. If he pushes the broom through 5.0 m, how much work does he do?

Step 1   Find the horizontal component of the force:

$$F = 6.5 \text{ N} \times \cos 55° = 3.7 \text{ N}$$

Step 2   Calculate the work done:

$$\textbf{work done } F\Delta x = \textbf{3.7 N} \times \textbf{5.0 m} = \textbf{19 J}$$

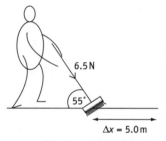

✓ *Quick check 1, 2*

Gravitational potential energy

When an object of mass m is raised (or lowered) through a height Δh, work is done and there is an increase (or decrease) in **gravitational potential energy**, ΔE_{grav}, given by:

$$\Delta E_{grav} = mg\Delta h$$

✓ *Quick check 3*

Kinetic energy

An object of mass m moving a speed v has kinetic energy E_k, given by:

$$E_k = \tfrac{1}{2}mv^2$$

✓ *Quick check 4*

Conservation of energy

When an object falls freely, there is a loss of gravitational potential energy that is *exactly* balanced by a gain in kinetic energy. This is an example of **energy conservation**. Energy cannot be created or destroyed so is never lost or gained overall. In situations where energy seems to 'disappear' it can always be accounted for, usually through heating.

Worked example

A skydiver of mass 75 kg falls freely from rest through a height of 40 m. How much kinetic energy does he gain, and what is his speed?

Later, with his parachute open, he falls through another 40 m with constant speed, i.e. no change in kinetic energy. By how much does his gravitational potential energy decrease? How is this 'lost' energy accounted for?

Step 1 Calculate change in energy:

gain in E_k = loss in E_{grav} = $mg\Delta h$ = 75 kg $\times$ 9.81 N kg^{-1} $\times$ 40 m = 2.9 $\times$ 10^4 J

Step 2 Calculate speed:

$$\tfrac{1}{2}mv^2 = E_k \text{ so } v^2 = \frac{2E_k}{m} = \frac{2 \times 2.9 \times 10^4 \text{ J}}{75 \text{ kg}} = 773.3 \text{ m}^2 \text{ s}^{-2} \text{ and } v = 28 \text{ m s}^{-1}$$

Step 3 ΔE_{grav} = 2.9 $\times$ 10^4 J as before. The energy is dissipated by heating the skydiver, his parachute and the air that he falls through.

✓ *Quick check 5*

Power

Power, P, is the rate of doing work or transferring energy.

$$P = \frac{\Delta W}{\Delta t}$$

Power has SI units of watts, W: 1 W = 1 J s^{-1}.

Worked example

An athlete does 10 press-ups in 2 minutes. Each involves 180 J of work. What is his average power?

Step 1 Calculate total work done:

Total ΔW = 10 $\times$ 180 J

Step 2 Write the equation for power and solve:

$$P = \frac{\Delta W}{\Delta t} = \frac{10 \times 180 \text{ J}}{120 \text{ s}} = 15 \text{ W}$$

✓ *Quick check 6*

? Quick check questions

1 A cook uses a force of 12 N to lift a bag of flour 0.80 m onto a shelf. How much work is done?

2 A boat is pulled into harbour by two cables. How much energy is transferred when moving the boat through 10 m?

3 A mountaineer of mass 85 kg (including kit) climbs through a height of 2.5 km. What is the increase in gravitational potential energy?

4 What is the kinetic energy of a car of mass 1.2 tonne travelling at 14 m s^{-1}?

5 A diver drops from a board 5.0 m high. What is her speed as she enters the water?

6 A girl of mass 50 kg sprints up a flight of stairs, gaining a height of 2.0 m in 2.5 s. What is her power?

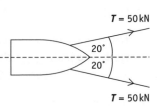

9

Projectile motion
HFS Part 5

A **projectile** is an object that moves through the air influenced only by the forces of gravity and air resistance. The horizontal and vertical *components* of its displacement, velocity and acceleration can be *treated separately* because they do not affect each other.

Often we can ignore air resistance when analysing projectile motion. A projectile influenced only by gravity moves in a parabolic path. In the multiflash picture both objects have vertical acceleration $g = 9.81$ m s^{-2}. The object on the right has a constant horizontal velocity.

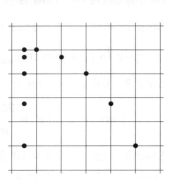

Worked example

A stunt car is driven horizontally off a cliff 50 m high at 25 m s^{-1}. How long does it take to fall into the sea? How far from the cliff does it crash?

Step 1 Consider vertical motion first. Acceleration $a = g = 9.81$ m s^{-2} (taking downwards as positive) and initial vertical velocity $u = 0$:

$$s = ut + \tfrac{1}{2} gt^2$$

$$s = \tfrac{1}{2} gt^2$$

Step 2 Rearrange and solve for t:

$$t^2 = \frac{2s}{g} = \frac{2 \times 50 \text{ m}}{9.81 \text{ m s}^{-2}} = 10.19 \text{ s}^2 \quad \text{so} \quad t = 3.2 \text{ s}$$

Step 3 Now consider horizontal motion. The horizontal velocity remains constant at $u = 25$ m s^{-1}:

$$s = ut = 25 \text{ m s}^{-1} \times 3.2 \text{ s} = 80 \text{ m}$$

✓ *Quick check 1–3*

Worked exam question[†]

It is possible to estimate the speed at which debris is ejected from a volcano by studying how far the blocks are thrown. The following passage is adapted from a description of a volcanic eruption:

The largest blasts ejected blocks 0.5 m to 1.0 m in diameter up to 1 km from the vent, suggesting ejection speeds of up to 100 m s^{-1}. The average ejection speed was probably about 60 m s^{-1}.

Q A block of debris is ejected at an angle of 40° to the horizontal from a vent at ground level. Show that the vertical component of its velocity is about 65 m s^{-1}.

[2]

A Vertical component = 100 m s^{-1} × sin 40° = 64.2 m s^{-1} which is close to 65 m s^{-1}.

▶ In 'show that ...' questions, do the complete calculation and compare your answer with the one given.

[†]The papers the worked exam questions in this guide are taken from are listed on the imprint page.

Q Find the time for which the block is in flight. [2]

A The block rises until its vertical velocity becomes zero: $v = 0$.

$a = -9.81$ m s^{-2} and $u = 64.2$ m s^{-1} (taking upwards as positive)

$$v = u + at \quad \text{so} \quad t = \frac{(v - u)}{a} = \frac{(0 - 64.2 \text{ m s}^{-1})}{-9.81 \text{ m s}^{-2}} = 6.5 \text{ s}$$

The block is in the air for twice the time taken to reach its maximum height, i.e. **13 s**.

If you had difficulty calculating the initial vertical velocity, use the 65 m s^{-1} given in the question.

Q Show that the distance the block is thrown is about 1 km. [3]

A Horizontal component of velocity $u = $ **100 m s^{-1} × cos 40° = 76.6 m s^{-1}**.

Horizontal velocity is constant, so distance travelled = **76.6 m s^{-1} × 13 s = 996 m**, which is about 1 km.

Q Studies of a crater left behind by a huge eruption suggest that the mass of material ejected was 6×10^{13} kg. Estimate the total kinetic energy of the ejected material. [2]

A From the information at the start of the question, average speed of ejection is about 60 m s^{-1}.

$$E_k = \tfrac{1}{2} mv^2 = \tfrac{1}{2} \times 6 \times 10^{13} \text{ kg} \times (60 \text{ m s}^{-1})^2 = 1 \times 10^{17} \text{ J}$$

Sometimes information you need near the end of a question is given near the beginning, so read the question carefully.

? Quick check questions

1 A Mars lander, cocooned within protective airbags, hits the surface of Mars. It bounces off the surface with a velocity of 10 m s^{-1} at an angle of 50° to the horizontal. The acceleration due to gravity is 3.7 m s^{-2}. How long does it take to reach its maximum height?

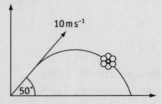

2 How far does the Mars lander travel horizontally before hitting the surface?

3 How high does the Mars lander bounce?

Electric circuits

SPC Sections 2.2 and 2.3

An electric **current** is a flow of **charged** particles.

$$I = \frac{\Delta Q}{\Delta t}$$

where I is current and ΔQ is the charge that flows past a point in a time interval Δt.

The SI unit of electric current is the ampere, A, and the SI unit of charge is the coulomb, C: $1\ A = 1\ C\ s^{-1}$.

Electric charge can be either positive or negative. Conventionally, the current *direction* is taken to be that of positive charge, though in metals current is a flow of electrons which have negative charge.

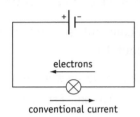
electrons
conventional current

- You will be expected to remember this relationship.
- The delta symbol, Δ, means 'the change in', 'the difference in' or 'a small amount of'.

✓ *Quick check 1*

Potential difference

Potential difference (pd) or **voltage**, V, is a measure of *energy transfer*. When a charge of 1 C moves through a pd of 1 V, then the energy transferred is 1 J.

$$E = W = QV$$

where E, or W, is the energy transferred or work done.

The SI unit of potential difference is the volt, V: $1\ V = 1\ J\ C^{-1}$.

The greater the pd across a device, the greater the current within it. Some devices *obey Ohm's law*, which means that current *is directly proportional to pd*. If the graph of pd against current is *not* a straight line going through the origin, then the device is non-ohmic.

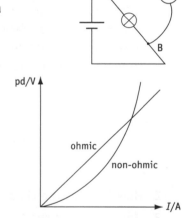

Resistance

Resistance R is defined as

$$R = \frac{V}{I}$$

The SI unit of resistance is the ohm, Ω: $1\ \Omega = 1\ V\ A^{-1}$.

For a given pd across a device, the greater the current, the smaller the resistance of the device. Resistance can be calculated from measurements of current and pd. The resistance of a device that obeys Ohm's law does not vary with current or pd.

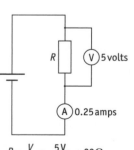
$R = \frac{V}{I} = \frac{5\,V}{0.25\,A} = 20\,\Omega$

✓ *Quick check 2*

Power

Power, P, is the rate of doing work or transferring energy.

$$P = \frac{\Delta W}{\Delta t}$$

The SI unit of power is the watt, W: $1\ \text{W} = 1\ \text{J s}^{-1}$.

In an electric circuit, $P = \left(\dfrac{W}{Q}\right) \times \left(\dfrac{Q}{t}\right)$, so

$$P = VI$$

and

$$W = VIt$$

As $V = IR$ and $I = V/R$,

$$P = I^2R = \frac{V^2}{R}$$

✓ **Quick check 3**

Efficiency

For any process or device:

efficiency = useful power (or energy) output/power (or energy) input

Efficiency is often expressed as a percentage.

Worked example

A solar-powered vehicle has a total area of 8 m^2 covered with solar cells that are 25% efficient. If the solar flux is 600 W m^{-2}, what is the useful power output from the solar cells?

Step 1 Calculate power input:

power input = 600 W m^{-2} $\times$ 8 m^2 = 4800 W

Step 2 Use the efficiency to calculate power output:

efficiency = 25% = 0.25, so useful power output = 0.25 $\times$ 4800 W = 1200 W

✓ **Quick check 4**

Quick check questions

1 A current of 2 A flows for 2 minutes. How much charge passes each point in the circuit?

2 For the non-ohmic device shown in the diagram on the right, calculate its resistance at two different points and hence say whether its resistance increases or decreases as pd is increased.

3 An electric kettle is rated 230 V, 2.5 kW.

   a What is the current in the element?

   b What is the resistance of the kettle's element?

   c If the element is replaced by one of higher resistance, will the power increase or decrease?

4 An electric motor is connected to a pd of 1.10 V and takes a current of 0.95 A. In a time 2.60 s it does 0.470 J of work to lift a load. What is the efficiency of the motor?

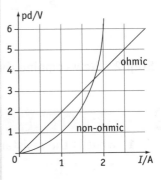

Combining resistors

SPC Section 2.2

Resistors in series

When resistors are joined together in **series** the current is the same throughout them all because the charge flowing into any point is the same as the charge flowing out. The total pd across the resistors is equal to the sum of the individual pds because it measures the total energy transferred by a coloumb of charge passing through all the resistors.

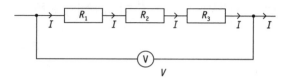

$$V = V_1 + V_2 + V_3 = IR_1 + IR_2 + IR_3 \text{ ...}$$

$$R_{total} = \frac{V}{I} = R_1 + R_2 + R_3 \text{ ... in series}$$

Resistors in parallel

When resistors are joined in **parallel**, the pd is the same across each one because the energy transferred by a coloumb of charge does not depend on the route it takes. The total current is equal to the sum of the individual currents because charge is neither created nor destroyed as it enters or leaves a junction.

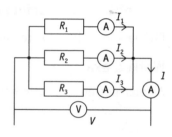

$$I = I_1 + I_2 + I_3 \text{ ...} = \frac{V}{R_1} + \frac{V}{R_2} + \frac{V}{R_3} \text{ ...}$$

$$\frac{I}{V} = \frac{1}{R_{total}} = \frac{1}{R_1} + \frac{1}{R_2} + \frac{1}{R_3} \text{ ... in parallel}$$

The total resistance is always *less* than the resistance of any one of the individual resistances joined in parallel.

Worked example

What is the total resistance in the circuit shown?

Step 1   Start with the resistors in parallel:

$$\frac{1}{R} = \frac{1}{4\,\Omega} + \frac{1}{8\,\Omega} = 0.25\ \Omega^{-1} + 0.125\ \Omega^{-1} = 0.375\ \Omega^{-1}$$

$$R = \frac{1}{0.375\ \Omega^{-1}} = 2.7\ \Omega$$

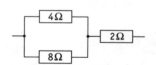

▶ Remember to add the reciprocals then find the reciprocal of the result.

Step 2   Now combine this with the other resistor in series.

$$2.7\ \Omega + 2\ \Omega = 4.7\ \Omega$$

✓ *Quick check 1*

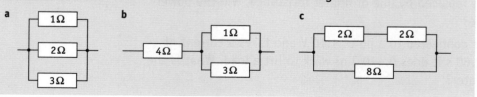

Resistance and temperature
SPC Section 3.2

The resistance of many electrical components *changes with temperature*. A current in a component can raise its temperature and so change its resistance.

Metals

The resistance of most metals *increases* with temperature.

- There are free electrons in metals.
- As electrons move through the metal they collide with vibrating atoms and are scattered.
- If the metal gets hotter, the atoms vibrate more vigorously.
- There are then more collisions between the atoms and the electrons.
- The flow of electrons is reduced, i.e. the current decreases.
- If the current decreases, the resistance has increased.

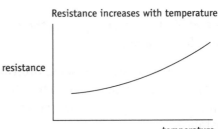

Resistance increases with temperature

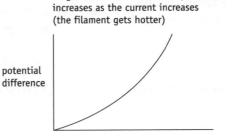

V against I for a filament lamp: resistance increases as the current increases (the filament gets hotter)

Semiconductors

Semiconductor materials contain far fewer free electrons than metals.

- Semiconductors with a *negative temperature coefficient* (NTC) have resistance that decreases with temperature. As the material gets hotter, increased vibration of the atoms releases more electrons. This increases the current: resistance has decreased.
- In semiconductors with *positive temperature coefficient* (PTC) the resistance increases with increasing temperature because the increase in collisions has a greater overall effect than the release of electrons.

✓ *Quick check 1, 2*

? *Quick check questions*

1 Sketch a graph of resistance against temperature for an NTC thermistor (temperature-sensitive resistor) and a graph of pd against current for the same device.

2 European Space Agency scientists tested a component used in a temperature warning circuit and obtained the results shown in the table. Plot a graph of the results and use it to answer these questions.

  a What was the resistance at 80 °C?

  b Which measurement was most likely to need re-checking?

  c Describe the relationship between resistance and temperature.

Temperature and resistance measurements

resistance/kΩ	1.4	2.1	3.8	6.0	6.5	9.2
temperature/°C	200	175	50	25	−25	−75

Internal resistance

SPC Sections 2.2 and 2.3

The **emf** $\mathscr{E}$ of a power supply is the *total* energy it supplies to each coloumb of charge.

Many power supplies have some **internal resistance**, so some of the energy supplied to each coloumb is 'lost' due to heating within the power supply. The figure shows how we represent a power supply with internal resistance.

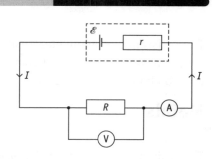

Energy supplied to each coloumb	=	energy transferred within load resistor	+	energy transferred due to internal heating

$$\mathscr{E} = IR + Ir = V + Ir$$

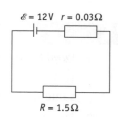

Practise drawing and labelling this circuit diagram from memory.

Terminal potential difference and lost volts

V is the **terminal potential difference**. Internal resistance is represented by *r*. *Ir* is sometimes known as the *lost volts*.

- An *open circuit* means that the power supply has no connection between its terminals, or is connected to a *very high resistance*, e.g. a voltmeter. Then $I = 0$ and $V = \mathscr{E}$.

- A *short circuit* means that the power supply terminals are joined by a connection with *no resistance*. Then $V = 0$ and $I = \dfrac{\mathscr{E}}{r}$.

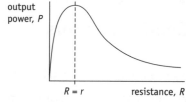

Maximum power output is achieved when the *load resistance* is the *same as the internal resistance* of the power supply.

Worked example

A power supply with emf 12.0 V and internal resistance 0.03 Ω operates a motor with a load resistance of 1.5 Ω. What is the current in the circuit? What are the 'lost volts' and what is the terminal pd?

$\mathscr{E} = 12V \quad r = 0.03\Omega$

$R = 1.5\Omega$

Step 1   Draw a diagram, showing R and r:

Step 2   Calculate the current:

$$\mathscr{E} = I (R + r) \quad \text{so} \quad I = \frac{\mathscr{E}}{(R + r)} = \frac{12.0 \text{ V}}{1.53 \ \Omega} = 7.84 \text{ A}$$

Step 3   Calculate the lost volts:

$$Ir = 7.84 \text{ A} \times 0.03 \ \Omega = 0.24 \text{ V}$$

Step 4   Calculate the terminal pd:

$$\text{terminal pd } V = IR = 7.84 \text{ A} \times 1.5 \ \Omega = 11.76 \text{ V}$$

$$\text{or} \quad V = \mathscr{E} - Ir = 12.0 \text{ V} - 0.24 \text{ V} = 11.76 \text{ V}$$

✓ *Quick check 1, 2*

Worked exam question

The makers of a solar panel list the following data about it:

- open-circuit voltage (emf)   20 V
- short-circuit current   3.4 A

The circuit shown is used for testing the panel.

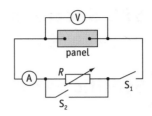

Q What would you expect the meters to read in the following situations?

   (i) With S_1 and S_2 both open as shown in the diagram?

   (ii) With S_1 and S_2 both closed?   [3]

A **(i)** Voltmeter reading 20 V; ammeter reading 0 A

   This is an open circuit. The terminal pd is equal to the emf and there is no current.

   (ii) Voltmeter reading 0 V; ammeter reading 3.4 A

   This is a short circuit, because the connecting wire in parallel with the variable resistor gives a combined resistance of zero. There is no resistance between the terminals and hence no terminal pd.

Q What is the internal resistance of the panel?   [2]

A When $V = 0$, $I = \dfrac{\mathscr{E}}{r}$, so

$$r = \frac{\mathscr{E}}{I} = \frac{20\ \text{V}}{3.4\ \text{A}} = 5.9\ \Omega$$

Q What will be the maximum output power from the panel?   [2]

A Power output is maximum when $R = r = 5.9\ \Omega$.

$$I = \frac{\mathscr{E}}{(R + r)} = \frac{20\ \text{V}}{11.8\ \Omega} = 1.7\ \text{A}$$

$$V = IR = 10\ \text{V}$$

$$P = VI = 17\ \text{W}$$

   Notice that here $V = \dfrac{\mathscr{E}}{2}$ and $I = \dfrac{\text{short-circuit current}}{2}$. This is always the case when the power output is maximum.

❓ Quick check questions

1 A resistor of 4.0 Ω is connected across a cell with emf 1.5 V and internal resistance 0.8 Ω.

   a What is the current in the circuit?

   b What is the terminal pd?

   c What is the power in the load resistor?

   d What is the power 'lost' in heating the cell?

2 Explain why the output power from a supply is zero if it is connected either in a short circuit or an open circuit.

Heating and cooling

SPC Sections 3.3 and 3.4

Specific heat capacity

The **specific heat capacity** of a material is the energy needed to change the temperature of 1 kg of the material by 1 °C.

$$\Delta E = mc\Delta\theta$$

where ΔE is the energy supplied or removed, m the mass of the sample, c the specific heat capacity of the material and $\Delta\theta$ the temperature change.

The SI units of specific heat capacity are J kg^{-1} °C^{-1}. For example, water has $c = 4.2 \times 10^3$ J kg^{-1} °C^{-1}.

Worked example

1.5 kg of water is heated in an electric kettle rated at 2 kW for 2 minutes. What is the greatest possible temperature rise of the water? Why is this temperature rise not likely to be achieved?

Step 1   Calculate energy input:

$$\Delta E = P\Delta t = 2 \times 10^3 \text{ J} \times 120 \text{ s} = 2.4 \times 10^5 \text{ J}$$

Step 2   Calculate temperature rise:

$$\Delta\theta = \frac{\Delta E}{mc} = \frac{2.4 \times 10^5 \text{ J}}{1.5 \text{ kg} \times 4.2 \times 10^3 \text{ J kg}^{-1}°\text{C}^{-1}} = 38.1 \text{ °C}$$

This temperature increase is unlikely to be achieved because some of the energy supplied will be used to heat the kettle (including the element) and the surroundings (conduction, convection and radiation).

Continuous flow heating and cooling

Many heating and cooling systems use the *continuous flow* of a fluid. In calculations involving such systems, it is useful to consider the changes that take place in a fixed time interval.

Worked example

A cooling system for a large computer uses water as the coolant. The input temperature of the water is 20 °C and the output temperature is 32 °C. The flow rate of the water is 2.0 kg per minute. What is the power of the cooling system?

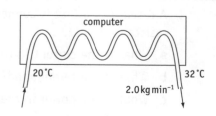

Step 1   In 1 minute, 2.0 kg of water is heated through 12 °C, so first calculate ΔE in 1 minute.

$$\Delta E = mc\Delta\theta = 2.0 \text{ kg} \times 4.2 \times 10^3 \text{ J kg}^{-1} °\text{C}^{-1} \times 12 \text{ °C} = 1.0 \times 10^5 \text{ J}$$

Step 2   Calculate the power:

$$P = \frac{\Delta E}{\Delta t} = \frac{1.0 \times 10^5 \text{ J}}{60 \text{ s}} = 1.7 \times 10^3 \text{ W}$$

Worked exam question

A teacher is demonstrating the power of different devices. She drills a hole in the wall for 30 s with a drill connected to the 230 V mains supply. The average current is 0.90 A. When she puts the drill down, the tip of the steel bit melts a hole in a plastic tray.

- mass of drill bit = 13 g
- specific heat capacity of steel = 510 J kg^{-1} $°C^{-1}$
- room temperature = 20 °C

Q Assume all the electrical energy is transferred to the bit where it produces heating. Calculate the temperature of the bit after the drilling. [3]

A **Energy supplied $\Delta E = VIt$ = 230 V $\times$ 0.90 A $\times$ 30 s = 6210 J**

$$\Delta\theta = \frac{\Delta E}{mc}$$

1 g = 10^{-3} kg, so 13 g = 13 $\times$ 10^{-3} kg = 0.013 kg.

$$\Delta\theta = 6210 \text{ J}/(0.013 \text{ kg} \times 510 \text{ J kg}^{-1}\text{ }°C^{-1}) = 937 \text{ }°C$$

Temperature of bit = 937 °C + 20 °C = 957 °C.

Q Discuss whether this is likely to be the actual temperature of the bit. [3]

A The actual temperature is likely to be *lower*. Some of the input energy will be transferred to the wall, to rest of the drill and to the surrounding air, so there will be less energy transferred to the bit.

When asked to 'discuss', try to be as precise as possible. Here, it's important to say whether you think the actual temperature will be higher or lower than calculated, and explain why. You are told what to assume for the calculation, so a good starting point is to say what will happen if the assumption is not correct.

> ◗ Remember to put the mass in kg and to add the initial temperature so as to find the final temperature. Be careful to include correct units, i.e. not just C and not just °.

✓ *Quick check 1, 2*

? ## Quick check questions

1 A student used an electric heater to heat a well-insulated 1.0 kg aluminium block, as shown in the diagram. The voltmeter reading was 12 V and the ammeter reading was 2.2 A. The block was heated for 5 minutes and the observed temperature rise was 8.6 °C. Assuming no energy losses, calculate the specific heat capacity of the aluminium.

2 A 200 W electric heater is used as the basis of a flow meter. Water flows in at 10 °C and out at 18 °C. Calculate the rate of flow of the water in g s^{-1}.

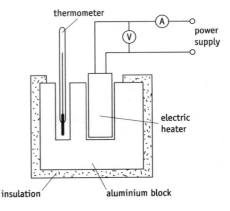

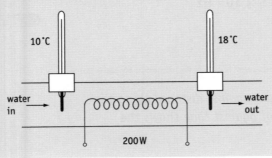

Oscillations and waves
MUS Sections 1.2 and 1.3

A **travelling wave** transfers energy by means of oscillations. An **oscillation** is a regular to-and-fro motion. Travelling waves can be transverse or longitudinal. In a **transverse** wave, there are oscillations *at right angles to* the direction of wave travel. A **longitudinal** wave involves oscillations *along* the direction of travel.

Transverse waves

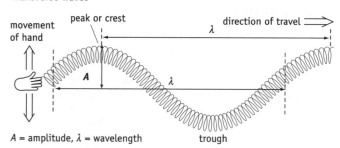

A = amplitude, λ = wavelength

Longitudinal waves

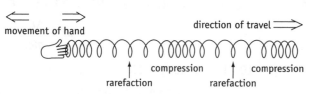

- The **amplitude** of a wave or an oscillation is the maximum displacement from the equilibrium position.

- The **wavelength** λ of a wave is the distance between two points that are oscillating in step or in **phase**, e.g. between two crests.

- **Frequency**, *f*, is the number of oscillations per second, or the number of complete waves passing a point in one second. The SI unit of frequency is the hertz, Hz: $1 \text{ Hz} = 1 \text{ s}^{-1}$.

- The **period**, *T*, is the time taken for one oscillation. $T = \dfrac{1}{f}$.

If *v* is the speed at which the wave travels, then

$$v = f\lambda$$

Worked example

Light from a red laser pointer has a wavelength of 670 nm. The speed of light in air is $3.0 \times 10^8 \text{ m s}^{-1}$. What is the frequency of the laser light?

Wavelength $\lambda = 670 \times 10^{-9}$ m.

$$f = \frac{v}{\lambda} = \frac{3.0 \times 10^8 \text{ m s}^{-1}}{670 \times 10^{-9} \text{ m}} = 4.5 \times 10^{14} \text{ Hz}$$

> **▶** Notice the conversion from nm to m.
> $1 \text{ nm} = 1 \times 10^{-9}$ m.

> ✓ *Quick check 1*

Representing waves

A wave can be represented by a graph of *displacement against distance* along the wave at one instant of time. A graph of *displacement against time* shows the oscillation at one position.

Worked example

The figure shows a wave travelling away from the origin.

- What is the wavelength? What is the period of the oscillation?

- Sketch graphs of displacement against time for the points A and B.

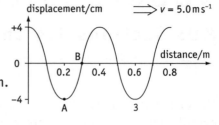

Step 1   From the graph, wavelength λ = distance between peaks = 0.40 m.

Step 2   Calculate the frequency:

$$\text{frequency } f = \frac{v}{\lambda} = \frac{5.0 \text{ ms}^{-1}}{0.40 \text{ m}} = 12.5 \text{ Hz}$$

Step 3   Calculate the period:

$$T = \frac{1}{f} = \frac{1}{12.5 \text{ Hz}} = 0.08 \text{ s}$$

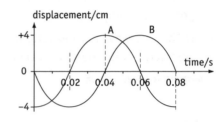

Step 4   The graph for A starts at a displacement of −4.0 cm. In the graph for B, the displacement starts at zero and initially becomes negative as time increases.

At first glance, graphs of displacement against distance or time look very similar. Use the labels on the axes to distinguish between them.

✓ *Quick check 2*

Sound waves

Sound waves are longitudinal waves. Molecules are displaced from their equilibrium positions to produce regions of **compression** (high pressure, point A) and **rarefaction** (low pressure, point B).

A displacement–distance graph for a *longitudinal* wave is usually drawn with the displacements at right angles to the direction of travel, even though the actual displacements are along the direction of travel.

Regions of maximum and minimum pressure coincide with positions of zero displacement. Compression is produced when particles are displaced towards one position from both directions, e.g. at point A where particles to the left of A are displaced to the right, and those to the right of A are displaced to the left. Rarefaction arises when particles are displaced in both directions away from one position, e.g. point B.

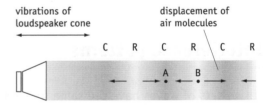

? *Quick check questions*

1 An experiment used a sound source of frequency 10 kHz. The speed of sound in air was found to be 338 m s^{-1}. What was the period of the oscillations producing the sound? What was the wavelength of the sound they produced?

2 A transverse wave of amplitude 10 cm and frequency 2.0 Hz travels along a rope at 1.6 m s^{-1}. Sketch a graph of displacement against distance for the wave and a second graph showing the motion of one point, starting from maximum positive displacement.

Superposition

MUS Sections 1.4 and 2.2

The **phase difference** between two waves or oscillations is often described using *angles*. A complete cycle is equivalent to an angle of 360° or 2π radians.

When two or more waves arrive at the same place at the same time, **superposition** takes place.

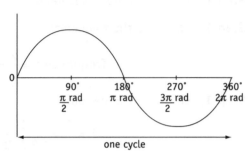

- If the waves are in phase, the superposition is *constructive* and produces a large amplitude.

- If the two waves are exactly half a cycle out of phase (i.e. in *antiphase*), *destructive* superposition occurs.

✔ *Quick check 1*

Constructive superposition

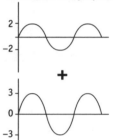 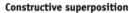 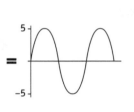

Destructive superposition

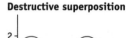 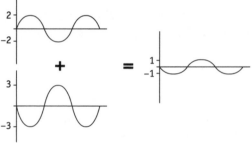

Interference patterns

If two sets of waves have the same frequency and an unchanging phase relationship they are said to be **coherent**. Superposition of coherent waves produces a steady *interference pattern*.

The figure shows waves from two loudspeakers connected to the same signal generator so that they are coherent. To reach point C, waves from A have travelled further than waves from B. The **path difference** is exactly equal to the wavelength, so waves arrive at point C *in phase*. A crest from A arrives at the same time as a crest from B, and a trough from A at the same time as a trough from B. *Constructive superposition* takes place, giving a loud sound.

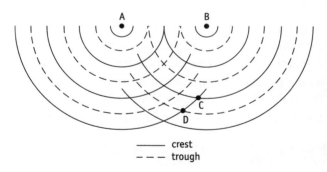

—— crest
– – – trough

Worked exam question

The diagram shows a cross-section through a compact disc. The metal layer of a CD is the recording surface and contains narrow ridges which form a spiral around the disc. *Monochromatic* laser light is used to read the CD. When the light meets a ridge some of it *interferes destructively* with light reflected from neighbouring valleys.

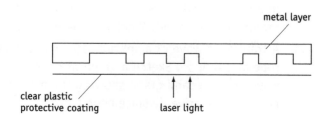

metal layer

clear plastic
protective coating

laser light

Q Explain the meaning of the words in italics in the passage above. [2]

A *Monochromatic* means single colour, i.e. single frequency/single wavelength.

Interferes destructively means that a crest and trough arrive together and cancel each other.

Q The wavelength of the light *within the plastic coating* is 500 nm. The height of the ridges on the CD is 125 nm. Explain how destructive interference occurs. [3]

A In the detector, light reflected from a ridge combines with light reflected from a valley. The path difference between the two sets of waves is twice the height of the ridge, i.e. 250 nm. The two sets of waves therefore arrive at the detector in antiphase, so destructive interference occurs.

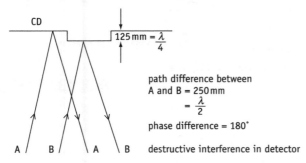

When asked to 'explain', make your answer as precise as possible by using technical terms and including numerical values.

Infrared lasers have been used for CDs because they are reliable and relatively inexpensive. Lasers are being developed that emit ultraviolet light with a wavelength about one half that of infrared lasers. They are known as 'blue light' lasers.

▶ Always include diagrams where they help your answer.

Q Will it be possible to play existing CDs using blue light laser CD players? Explain your answer. [2]

A No. A CD player works by detecting an on/off **digital signal** as it scans the disc. With a blue light laser, the path difference of 250 nm between the two sets of reflected waves would be equal to the wavelength so interference would always be constructive. The signal in the detector would always be 'on' and so would carry no useful information.

❓ Quick check questions

1 Sketch the superposition of two waves with equal amplitude that have a phase difference of π radians.

2 Using the words *phase* or *antiphase*, *path difference*, *superposition*, and other suitable terms, explain what happens at point D in the figure on the opposite page.

3 Lasers and other light sources emit in short bursts each lasting no more than a few nanoseconds. Suppose two lasers that emit exactly the same wavelength produce overlapping spots of light on a screen. Using the words *coherent* and *phase*, explain why there is *no* steady interference pattern.

Standing waves
MUS Sections 1.4, 1.5 and 1.6

Whenever a wave meets a boundary, it is *reflected*.

If a wave travelling along a string is reflected at a fixed end, there is a phase change of 180° (π radians).

If a wave is repeatedly reflected, *superposition* of the incident and reflected waves can produce a **standing wave** where all oscillations are exactly in phase or in antiphase. Positions of *no* oscillation are called **nodes**. **Antinodes** are where the oscillations have maximum amplitude. The distance between neighbouring nodes is *half the wavelength* of the travelling wave.

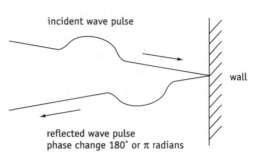

incident wave pulse

wall

reflected wave pulse
phase change 180° or π radians

✓ Quick check 1

Standing waves on a string

A *standing wave on a string* has a node at each end. For any particular string, there is a series of frequencies that can produce standing waves. The lowest frequency is the *fundamental frequency*. For any standing wave, half the wavelength must fit along the string a whole number of times.

The wavelength is related to frequency via the speed, *v*, of waves travelling *along the string*:

$$v = \sqrt{\frac{T}{\mu}}$$

where *T* is the tension in the string (N) and μ its mass per unit length (kg m^{-1}).

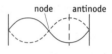

node   antinode

$\lambda/2$

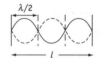

l

—— and ---- are positions of the string ½ a time period apart

Worked example

A musical instrument has strings 80 cm long under a tension of 10 N. One string's mass per unit length is 4×10^{-4} kg m^{-1}.

What is the speed of travelling waves on the string?

What is the frequency of the fundamental note produced?

What happens to the pitch (frequency) of the note if the tension is increased? Explain why this occurs.

Step 1 Calculate wave speed:

$$v = \sqrt{\frac{10\ \text{N}}{4 \times 10^{-4}\ \text{kg m}^{-1}}} = 158\ \text{m s}^{-1}$$

Step 2 Use wavelength λ and wave speed *v* to calculate frequency:

$$\lambda = 2 \times 80\ \text{cm} = 1.60\ \text{m} \quad \text{so} \quad f = \frac{v}{\lambda} = \frac{158\ \text{m s}^{-1}}{1.60\ \text{m}} = 98.8\ \text{Hz}$$

The pitch rises. Increasing tension increases the wave speed, so for the *same wavelength on the string*, the frequency must be higher.

✓ Quick check 2, 3

Standing waves in a tube or pipe

If a sound wave is travelling in a tube, either an open or a closed end of the tube acts as a boundary and reflection takes place. A closed end produces a displacement node and an open end produces a displacement antinode.

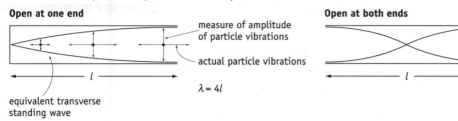

Open at one end

measure of amplitude of particle vibrations

actual particle vibrations

equivalent transverse standing wave

l

$\lambda = 4l$

Open at both ends

$\lambda = 2l$

l

Worked example

A pipe, open at both ends, is 2.0 metres long. What are the wavelength and frequency of the fundamental note produced? (Assume the speed of sound in air is 330 m s^{-1}.)

Step 1   Calculate the wavelength:

$$\lambda = 2 \times 2.0 \text{ m} = 4.0 \text{ m}$$

Step 2   Calculate the frequency:

$$f = \frac{v}{\lambda} = \frac{330 \text{ m s}^{-1}}{4.0 \text{ m}} = 82.5 \text{ Hz}$$

> ❶ Think where the nodes and antinodes will be in an open pipe.

> ✓ *Quick check 4–6*

❓ Quick check questions

1 The reflection of microwaves inside a microwave oven gives rise to a standing wave pattern. If the rotating turntable is removed and a tray of sliced cheese is put into the microwave oven, after a few moments a pattern of 'hot spots' can be observed where the cheese has melted. If the microwave frequency is 2450 MHz and the distance between adjacent 'hot spots' is 6 cm, calculate the velocity of the microwaves.

2 Explain what happens to the pitch of the note if the string in the Worked example on page 24 is replaced by one with greater mass per unit length.

3 The speed of waves along a string is 200 m s^{-1} and the string is 90 cm long. What is the frequency of the standing wave that has *three* antinodes?

4 If the pipe in the Worked example above is replaced by one with a closed end, what are the wavelength and frequency of the new fundamental note?

5 Pan pipes have tubes that are open at both ends. Compare the frequencies of the fundamental notes produced by tubes that are 6 cm and 12 cm long.

6 Sketch a diagram showing one of the standing waves with *higher* frequency than the fundamental frequency inside a tube with one closed end. Write down the relationship between the length of the tube and the wavelength of the wave.

Lenses

MUS Section 2.4 and 2.5

Converging or convex *lenses* refract (bend) rays of light. If the rays are *parallel to the axis of the lens*, they converge at the *principal focus*. The distance to this point from the centre of the lens is the **focal length**, *f*, of the lens.

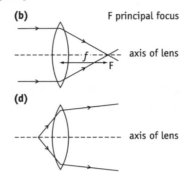

If a lens is at a very large distance from a point source of light, the rays that enter the lens will be parallel.

Power of a lens

The more powerful a lens, the shorter its focal length.

$$P = \frac{1}{f}$$

where *P* is the **power** of a lens.

The unit of lens power is the dioptre, D: $1\ D = 1\ m^{-1}$.

✓ *Quick check 1*

Ray diagrams

The size and position of an *image* produced by a lens can be predicted by drawing an accurate **ray diagram**:

- Draw the lens and the principal axis at right angles to each other.
- Mark the focal points, F, of the lens on both sides.
- Draw a line at right angles to the axis to represent the object, O.
- Draw two rays of light from the top of the object as shown in the figures:

    A ray ① that travels through the centre of the lens and continues in the same direction.

    A ray ② which is parallel to the principal axis and is refracted to pass through the principal focus on the other side.

❶ It is usual to represent the lens by a straight line.

❶ If the lens is shown as an actual lens shape, ignore its curved surfaces and draw the change in direction as the rays cross a line through the centre of the lens.

- Draw a line to represent the image, I. The point where the rays ① and ② cross, or appear to originate, marks the image of the top of the object.

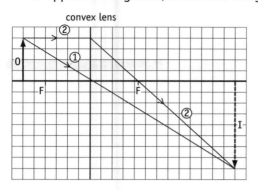

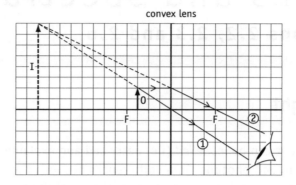

Forming a real image   Forming a virtual image

When a lens forms an image on a screen, light from each point in the object produces a corresponding point of light in the image. This type of image is called a *real image*.

If the lens–object distance is less than the focal length of a convex lens, the rays do not cross but appear to originate from a point behind the lens. Such an image is called a *virtual image* and cannot be produced on a screen.

- *Practise drawing accurate ray diagrams.*
- *Use graph paper and choose a sensible scale for the drawing.*
- *Use a ruler and a sharp pencil.*
- *Make corrections by rubbing out, not by crossing out.*
- *Label the lens, object and image.*
- *Add arrows to show the direction of the rays.*
- *Use dashed lines to extend rays back to a virtual image.*

? Quick check question

1 Compare the power of two converging lenses with focal lengths of 20 cm and 40 cm.

Photons and spectra

MUS Sections 2.2, 2.3 and 2.6

Modelling light

The behaviour of light can be *modelled* (i.e. described and explained) in two different ways: *waves* and **photons**. Some differences between the models are shown in the table. Photons are packets of energy or 'particles' of light.

wave model	photon model
colour depends on frequency	colour depends on energy
frequency of ⟩ frequency of blue light red light wavelength of ⟨ wavelength of blue light red light	a blue photon has more energy than a red photon

The two models are linked by the relationship

$$E = hf$$

where E is the photon energy (J), f the wave frequency (Hz) and h the Planck constant (J s).

Worked example

Light of a certain orange colour has wavelength 589 nm. What is the energy of one photon of this light? (Planck constant $h = 6.63 \times 10^{-34}$ J s; speed of light $c = 3.00 \times 10^8$ m s^{-1}.)

Step 1 Use the equations relating frequency, speed, wavelength and energy:

$$f = \frac{c}{\lambda} \quad \text{and} \quad E = hf, \quad \text{so} \quad E = \frac{hc}{\lambda}$$

Step 2 Convert wavelength to m:

$$\lambda = 589 \text{ nm} = 589 \times 10^{-9} \text{ m}$$

Step 3 Substitute values and solve:

$$E = \frac{6.63 \times 10^{-34} \text{ J s} \times 3.00 \times 10^8 \text{ m s}^{-1}}{589 \times 10^{-9} \text{ m}} = 3.38 \times 10^{-19} \text{ J}$$

> Remember always to express the wavelength in m.

> ✓ *Quick check 1, 2*

Spectra and energy levels

When light is spread out into its separate colours a *spectrum* is observed. If the light is from a gas discharge tube, we observe a **line spectrum**, i.e. only certain lines of distinct colour are present, separated by gaps.

Line spectra can be explained using the photon model. Each coloured line arises when an electron within an atom drops from one energy level to another and a photon is emitted.

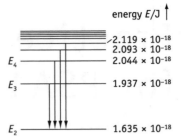

The photon energies can be calculated from measurements of the wavelengths emitted. These photon energies correspond to the *differences* between energy levels. Each atom has its own unique set of discrete (separate) electronic energy levels and hence its own unique line spectrum.

An energy level diagram is like a graph with energy increasing upwards. A downward-pointing arrow represents an electron losing energy and giving out a photon. The figure shows some of the transitions for a hydrogen atom.

Worked example

Calculate the frequency of light emitted by a transition from level E_3 to level E_2 in the figure above.

Step 1 Find the difference in energy between levels:

$$E_3 = 1.937 \times 10^{-18} \text{ J}, E_2 = 1.635 \times 10^{-18} \text{ J}$$

The energy lost by the electron is $E_3 - E_2$, so photon energy

$$E = E_3 - E_2 = 0.302 \times 10^{-18} \text{ J}$$

Step 2 Calculate the frequency:

$$\text{frequency } f = \frac{E}{h} = \frac{3.02 \times 10^{-19} \text{ J}}{6.63 \times 10^{-34} \text{ Js}} = 4.56 \times 10^{14} \text{ Hz}$$

✓ *Quick check 3*

? Quick check questions

1 Complete the table to compare the properties of light in various parts of the spectrum.

Comparing values

colour	typical wavelength/nm	frequency/Hz	photon energy/J
ultraviolet	300		
blue	410		
red	660		
infrared	800		

2 A red laser pointer is described as 670 nm, 5 mW.

  a What is the energy of a single photon?

  b How many photons leave the pointer in a single second?

3 Suppose three of the energy levels in an atom have energies $E_1 = 1.345 \times 10^{-18}$ J, $E_2 = 1.579 \times 10^{-18}$ J and $E_3 = 1.654 \times 10^{-18}$ J. What are the energies of the photons that could be emitted by transitions between these levels? What are the frequencies and wavelengths of the emitted light?

Practice exam questions for PSA1

1 An instrument called a Dynamometer is used to test the performance of trains. It can measure and record, amongst other factors, a train's speed, acceleration, power and distance travelled, together with the time at which the measurements were taken.

The graph below shows a record for a train of mass 200 000 kg until it reached its maximum speed of 35 m s^{-1}.

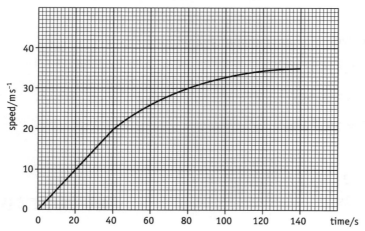

Between what times was the train's acceleration uniform?   [1]

What was the magnitude of this uniform acceleration?   [1]

What was the magnitude of the instantaneous acceleration at t = 80 s?   [2]

What was the magnitude of the acceleration at t = 140 s?   [1]

Calculate the size of the net force that produced the uniform acceleration. [1]

How far had the train travelled during the interval from t = 0 to t = 40 s? [2]

From Edexcel Pilot specimen paper, Unit PSA1   [Total: 8]

2 The forces acting on the hands and feet of a rock climber change continually as the climber moves across the rock face.

A climber of mass 70 kg who is carrying a rucksack of mass 20 kg is in the process of moving his right foot to a new toehold. In the diagram he is shown temporarily at rest whilst looking for a suitable position for his foot.

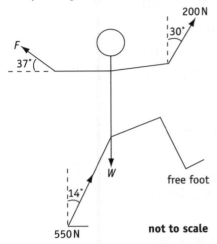

What is the total weight *W* of the climber and his load? [2]

Show that the vertical components of the 200 N and 550 N forces add up to approximately 700 N. [2]

The climber is in equilibrium. What do you understand by the term *equilibrium*? [1]

Calculate the magnitude of force *F*. [2]

The climber sees a suitable position and accelerates his free foot vertically upwards. Discuss the effect this might have on the force exerted on the other foot. [2]

From Edexcel January 1999, Unit PSA1 [Total: 9]

3 A tennis machine serves tennis balls over the net for a player to practise return shots.

The ball emerges horizontally 2.50 m above the ground with velocity *v* and hits the ground 21.0 m away from the machine as shown in the diagram above.

Ignoring air resistance show that the ball takes 0.714 s to reach the ground. [2]

Calculate the velocity *v* with which the ball left the machine. [2]

Calculate the vertical component of the velocity of the ball when it reaches the ground. [1]

State the horizontal component of the velocity of the ball when it reaches the ground. [1]

Find the angle at which the ball strikes the ground. [3]

What would be the effect on this angle of taking air resistance into account? Explain your answer. [1]

From Edexcel June 1999, Unit PSA1 [Total: 10]

4 Satellites can be used for a wide variety of purposes including communications and surveying.

In order to enable companies to use these facilities by purchasing their own craft, microspacecraft have been developed. These are much cheaper to build and launch since they are small and need little power to operate.

In order to keep the craft as small as possible, compact batteries must be used. Different battery systems can be compared by considering their energy density, measured in Wh m^{-3}.

Explain why the Wh m^{-3} is an appropriate unit in which to measure energy density. [2]

One such battery has a terminal potential difference of 6.0 V when supplying 90 W to the equipment on board.

   (i)   Calculate the current in the battery. [2]

   (ii) The internal resistance of the battery is 0.020 Ω. Show that the emf of the battery is 6.3 V. [2]

   (iii) Calculate the power loss in the battery. [1]

   (iv) State what happens to this power. [1]

   (v)   Calculate the efficiency of the battery at this current. [1]

The same power can be supplied using solar cells. The efficiency of these cells is 10% and the solar flux is 1.4 kW m^{-2}. Calculate the minimum area of solar cells required to supply 90 W. [2]

Explain why this is the *minimum* area required. [1]

From Edexcel June 1999, Unit PSA1 [Total: 12]

5 The passage below is taken from marketing material supplied by a manufacturer of electrically heated showers.

> *Most electric showers draw cold water direct from the main supply and heat it as it is used – day or night. Not only are they particularly useful for those who do not have a stored hot water supply, but they are versatile because every home can have one.*

Describe the energy transfer which takes place in an electric shower. [2]

Write an equation for the energy transfer you have described. [1]

The technical data supplied by one manufacturer states that their most powerful shower system is fitted with a 10.8 kW heating element and can deliver up to 16 litres of water per minute.

Show that the showering temperature is about 25 °C if the temperature of the mains water is 15 °C and the shower is used at its maximum settings.

(Specific heat capacity of water = 4200 J kg^{-1} K^{-1}. Mass of 1 litre of water = 1.0 kg.) [3]

The marketing material includes the statement:

> *Please remember that during the colder months, flow rates may need to be reduced to allow for the cooler temperature of incoming cold water.*

Calculate the approximate flow rate required for an output temperature of 25 °C when the incoming water temperature is 5 °C [2]

The maximum steady current drawn by the unit is about 45 A. However, when the shower is first turned on the current is much higher for a short time. Suggest a possible explanation. [1]

From Edexcel June 1999, Unit PSA1 [Total: 9]

6 The diagram shows a sketch of an electron-microscope image of the world's smallest guitar.

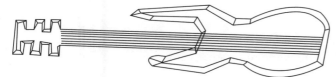

Its strings have a length of 10 millionths (10×10^{-6}) of a metre. They have a width of about 50 billionths (50×50^{-9}) of a metre – the size of approximately 100 atoms. Plucking the tiny strings would produce a high-pitched sound at the inaudible frequency of approximately 10 MHz. The guitar was made by researchers at Cornell University with a single silicon crystal; this tiny guitar is a playful example of nanotechnology.

Explain briefly why a vibrating string creates a sound wave. [2]

Comment on the phrase 'the inaudible frequency of approximately 10 MHz'. [1]

When the string of this guitar vibrates at its fundamental frequency (10 MHz), what is the wavelength of the waves on the string? State **one** assumption you are making. [2]

What is the speed of the waves along the string? [2]

The string has a mass per unit length of 4×10^{-12} kg m^{-1}. Calculate the tension in the string. [2]

From Edexcel January 2000, Unit PSA1 [Total: 9]

7 Astronomers can identify different gases present in the outer parts of stars by analysing the line spectra of the starlight.

Explain the meaning of line spectra. [2]

Explain how line spectra provide evidence for the existence of energy levels in atoms. [3]

From Edexcel January 2001, Unit PSA1 [Total: 5]

8 Large convex lenses are sold by opticians as magnifiers for reading. A typical reading magnifier has a focal length of 30 cm.

On the grid like that shown below, complete a scale ray diagram to show the formation of an image by a convex lens of focal length 30 cm used as a reading magnifier. The object is 15 cm away from the lens.

[Scale: 1 square = 5 cm]

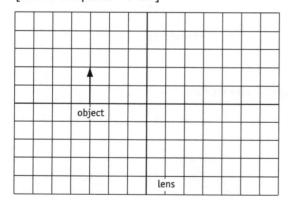

[3]

What is the image distance? [1]

Magnification is defined as Image size/Object size.

Take measurements from your diagram to calculate the magnification of this image. [2]

From Edexcel June 2000, Unit PSA1 [Total: 6]

Unit PSA2: Physics for Life

This unit tests:

- **Digging up the Past (DIG)**
- **Good Enough to Eat (EAT)**
- **Spare Part Surgery (SUR)**

In this unit, some areas of physics are studied in more than one place – for example, properties of materials is met in EAT and again in SUR. To help you bring the ideas together as part of your revision, this part of the revision guide is structured around the physics content rather than following the order of your textbook. The heading of each spread indicates the physics content covered and there is a reference to the relevant section(s) of your textbook where you will find further details.

Resistance and resistivity

DIG Section 1.2

Materials have **resistivity**. Objects have *resistance*. For any given material a short, fat sample has a low resistance, R, whereas a long, thin sample has a high resistance.

$$R = \frac{\rho l}{A}$$

where l is the length of the sample, A its cross-sectional area and ρ the resistivity of the material.

The SI units of resistivity are $\Omega\ m^2/m$, i.e. $\Omega\ m$.

> ▶ You will be expected to remember this relationship.

Conductivity

Conductivity $\sigma = 1/\rho$. It has SI units $1/(\Omega\ m)$, i.e. $\Omega^{-1}\ m^{-1}$.

> ✓ *Quick check 1*

Worked example

Copper has resistivity $1.7 \times 10^{-8}\ \Omega\ m$. What is the resistance of a copper wire with diameter 1.6 mm and length 5.0 m?

Step 1 Convert units to m:

$$\text{diameter} = 1.6 \times 10^{-3}\ \text{m, radius } r = 0.8 \times 10^{-3}\ \text{m}$$

Step 2 Write the equation for R and substitute:

$$R = \frac{\rho l}{A} = \frac{\rho l}{\pi r^2} = \frac{1.7 \times 10^{-8}\ \Omega\ m \times 5.0\ m}{\pi \times (0.8 \times 10^{-3}\ m)^2} = 4.2 \times 10^{-2}\ \Omega$$

> ▶ In calculating the cross-sectional area of a wire, be careful to use its radius, not its diameter. Take care with units; express the radius in m so that you get the area in m^2.

> ✓ *Quick check 2*

Values of resistivity

The figure shows the resistivities of some materials plotted on a logarithmic scale. Such a graph would be impossible to draw with a linear scale because the values cover such a large range. For example:

$$\rho_{copper} = 1.70 \times 10^{-8}\ \Omega\ m,\ \log_{10} \rho_{copper} = -7.77$$

$$\rho_{glass} = 1.96 \times 10^{11}\ \Omega\ m,\ \log_{10} \rho_{glass} = +11.3$$

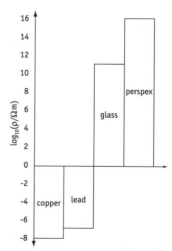

? *Quick check questions*

1 Write down an equation to calculate ρ using measured values of R, l and A.

2 A glass rod 10 cm long and 5.0 mm in diameter has resistance $1.0 \times 10^{15}\ \Omega$. What is the resistivity of this glass?

3 Carbon has resistivity $1.6 \times 10^{-5}\ \Omega\ m$. What value should be plotted for carbon on the figure to the right?

> ✓ *Quick check 3*

Potential dividers

DIG Section 1.3

In the circuit shown here, the potential difference (pd) across each resistor is proportional to its resistance, and the sum of the pds across all the resistors is equal to the pd between the terminals of the supply.

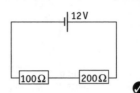

✓ *Quick check 1*

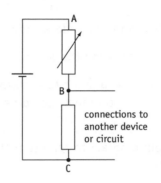

connections to another device or circuit

This circuit can be used as a *potential divider*. It can provide a pd to another device or another circuit, which is less than the pd of the power supply. If one of the resistors is variable, the pd from the potential divider can easily be adjusted.

✓ *Quick check 2*

Potential divider using resistance wire

A potential divider circuit can be made using a single piece of resistance wire. If a *uniform* wire is used, the resistance between any two points is proportional to the distance between them. When the wire carries a current, the graph of pd between one end and any other point is a straight line.

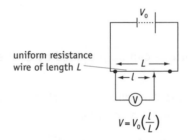

uniform resistance wire of length L

$$V = V_0\left(\frac{l}{L}\right)$$

Uniform wire

If the wire has a *non-uniform* cross-section, the resistance of a thin section of wire is greater than the resistance of a thick section of the same length. When the wire is carrying a current, the graph of pd against distance from one end is no longer a straight line.

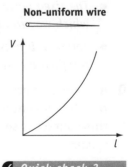

Non-uniform wire

✓ *Quick check 3*

Worked exam question

The volume control of a radio generally uses a linear potential divider to provide an adjustable voltage to the speaker.

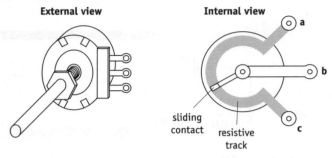

External view   **Internal view**

sliding contact   resistive track

a

b

c

The potential divider is used to provide a variable output voltage from a 9 V supply.

Q Draw a circuit diagram showing the potential divider connected to the supply.

Label your diagram with **a**, **b** and **c** to correspond to the terminals indicated above. Show which of the terminals could be used to provide the variable output voltage.   [2]

Add a resistor to your diagram to represent the speaker and label it S.   [1]

A

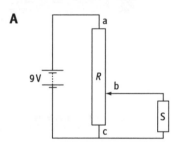

The variable output voltage can be provided by connecting between **a** and **b** or between **b** and **c**.

- *Practise drawing circuit diagrams such as this one from memory. Use a ruler and a sharp pencil to produce a neat diagram.*

- *Make sure you are familiar with this symbol for a potential divider. The arrow represents the sliding contact.*

- *The fixed power supply is connected to terminals **a** and **c**. It does not matter which way round it is connected.*

- *Terminal **b** must be the sliding contact. The speaker S must be connected to terminal **b** and one of the other terminals (it does not matter which one).*

Q A linear potential divider has a track which has equal changes of resistance when the sliding contact is rotated through equal angles. State the output voltage if this contact is set one half of the way round the track before connecting the speaker.   [1]

A 4.5 V

Q When the speaker is connected, the output voltage changes. Explain why.   [2]

A When the speaker is connected, its resistance is in parallel with half of the resistive track. The combined resistance of two resistors in parallel is less than the resistance of either one on its own. So the total resistance between **b** and **c** is less than half that of the resistive track. Therefore the pd between **b** and **c** is less than half the pd between **a** and **c**.

- *You sometimes need to use PSA1 work in PSA2, e.g. combining resistors in parallel.*

- *In questions that ask for an explanation, try to word your answer as clearly and precisely as possible in order to demonstrate your knowledge and understanding. Read through what you have written and think whether it would make sense to someone who did not already know what you were trying to say. If an examiner cannot make sense of what you have written, you will get no marks.*

- *In this example there are two marks, so make sure you say at least two things that are relevant and correct.*

Q The potential divider has a total resistance of 2.0 kΩ and is made from wire wound onto a support. The wire has a circular cross-section of diameter 2.0×10^{-4} m and resistivity 4.9×10^{-7} Ω m. Calculate the length of wire needed. [3]

A
$$R = \frac{\rho l}{A} \quad \text{so} \quad l = \frac{RA}{\rho}$$

$$\text{radius} = 1.0 \times 10^{-4}\text{ m}, \quad \text{so} \quad A = \pi r^2 = \pi \times (1.0 \times 10^{-4}\text{ m})^2$$

$$R = 2.0 \times 10^3 \text{ Ω}$$

$$l = \frac{2.0 \times 10^3 \text{ Ω} \times \pi \times (1.0 \times 10^{-4}\text{ m})^2}{4.9 \times 10^{-7} \text{ Ω m}}$$

$$= 128 \text{ m}$$

- *You need to rearrange the resistivity equation to make length l the subject. Make sure you know how to rearrange equations.*

- *To calculate area you need to halve the diameter to find the radius. You are expected to know how to calculate the area of a circle.*

- *You could calculate the area separately before putting it into the equation. $A = \pi \times 10^{-8}\text{ m}^2$.*

- *Remember to put R in Ω not kΩ.*

- *Take care with units and powers of ten.*

? Quick check questions

1 What is the pd across the 100 Ω resistor in the figure below?

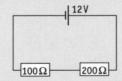

2 As the variable resistance of the potential divider shown to the right is *increased*, what happens to the pd between connections B and C?

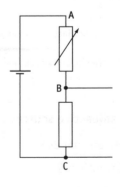

3 Sketch a graph of pd against distance from 0 for the wire in the figure below.

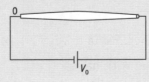

Nuclear radiation

DIG Section 3.3

The three *nuclear radiations* are all emitted randomly from the nuclei of radioactive atoms.

name and symbol	description	penetrating power	ionising ability
alpha, α	helium nucleus (2 protons plus 2 neutrons) positive charge	up to 10 cm in air or 0.1 mm in aluminium	heavily ionising
beta, β	electron negative charge	up to 1.5 m in air or 5 mm in aluminium	moderately ionising
gamma, γ	electromagnetic wave, wavelength less than about 10^{-11} m uncharged	several km in air 10 mm of lead absorbs about 50% of the radiation	weakly ionising

Make sure you know which Greek letter represents which type of radiation.

Background radiation

The environment around us is permeated by **background radiation**, which is nuclear radiation from various sources. Cosmic radiation, mainly from the Sun, has always been present, as has radiation from rocks such as granite and radon gas. More recently, background radiation has come from the testing of atomic bombs and catastrophic accidents in nuclear power stations.

✓ *Quick check 1*

Worked exam question

Aluminium foil is produced in a rolling mill as shown in the diagram below. The spacing of the rollers controls the thickness of the foil.

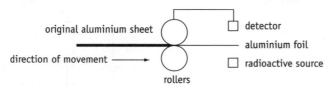

radioactive source	radiation emitted
Americium 241	α
Strontium 90	β
Cobalt 60	γ
Radium 226	α, β and γ

Q A radioactive source is used to monitor the thickness of the aluminium foil. For each source listed above, explain briefly whether it is suitable for this purpose in the rolling mill. [4]

A **Americium 241**   Not suitable. All the radiation would be absorbed, regardless of the thickness of the foil.

Strontium 90   Suitable. The amount of radiation absorbed will depend on the thickness of the foil.

Cobalt 60   Not suitable. Very little of the radiation will be absorbed, regardless of the thickness of the foil.

Radium 226   Not suitable. The beta radiation absorption will depend on foil thickness, but any changes will probably be masked by the gamma.

Try to word your answers so that they demonstrate your knowledge. For example, saying 'beta penetration is OK' is too vague and does not show that you really understand that absorption will vary with thickness of foil.

Q The signal at the detector increases. State and explain the change that would be needed to the spacing between the rollers to maintain the thickness of the foil. [1]

A The sheet is not absorbing enough radiation so it must be too thin. The rollers need to be moved further apart.

? *Quick check question*

1 For each of the following, say which type(s) of nuclear radiation it applies to.

   a is present in background radiation

   b is emitted from nuclei of atoms

   c can be absorbed by a single sheet of paper

   d can penetrate several cm aluminium

   e can penetrate several cm into an object, and causes significant ionisation as it does so.

Thermoluminescence
DIG Section 3.2

Thermoluminescence can occur after certain materials, most usually electrical insulators, have been irradiated by nuclear radiation. This damages the material, producing extra energy levels known as **defect levels**, and excites electrons in the material into the defect levels where they become trapped.

If the material is subsequently heated the trapped electrons return to their stable energy levels, emitting *visible radiation*. The intensity of this thermoluminescent glow (heat-induced emission of light) depends upon the number of electrons that have been trapped in the defect levels. This in turn depends upon the *radiation dose* received.

Worked exam question

Thermoluminescence can be used for dating old artefacts and so finding out how long ago humans lived in an area.

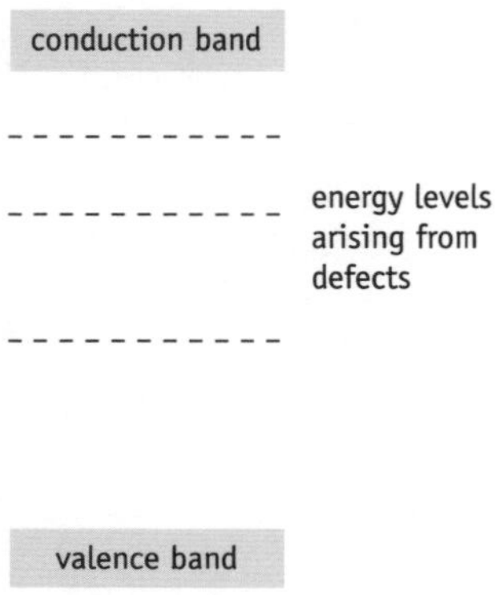

conduction band

- - - - - - - - - -

- - - - - - - - - - energy levels
arising from
defects

- - - - - - - - - -

valence band

Q The diagram above shows some energy levels in an old artefact. Suggest how electrons are provided with energy to rise to defect levels in artefacts buried underground. [1]

A Nuclear radiation from radioactive materials in the soil transfers energy to the electrons.

Q Radiation is emitted from the artefact when electrons make transitions from the defect levels. Draw an arrow on the diagram to represent the transition needed for the highest frequency of radiation to be emitted. [1]

A The arrow must be drawn from the highest defect level to the bottom of the valence band.

- *The arrow must point downwards because the electron loses energy. It must be as long as possible, because the greater the energy lost, the higher the frequency of the emitted light.*

- *The question refers to electrons making transitions 'from the defect levels' so the arrow must start from the highest one of these.*

Q Calculate the wavelength of this emitted radiation when the energy transition is 4.2×10^{-19} J. [3]

A
$$c = f\lambda \quad \text{so} \quad f = \frac{c}{\lambda}$$

$$E = hf \quad \text{so} \quad E = \frac{hc}{\lambda}$$

$$\text{hence } \lambda = \frac{ch}{E} = \frac{3.00 \times 10^8 \text{ m s}^{-1} \times 6.63 \times 10^{-34} \text{ J s}}{4.2 \times 10^{-19} \text{ J}}$$

$$= 4.7 \times 10^{-7} \text{ m}$$

- *You are asked to calculate the wavelength. Start by thinking how to calculate frequency, but don't stop there.*

- *You are expected to know the relationship between speed, frequency and wavelength. The relationship between energy and frequency is listed in the exam paper, as are the values of the speed of light and the Planck constant. Make sure you are familiar with these lists.*

- *It is advisable to do all the algebra before putting in any values, but you could start by calculating the frequency if you preferred.*

Q Explain why the artefact emits radiation with a range of frequencies. [2]

A There are several possible energy transitions, each giving rise to a different frequency. Electrons can start from any of the defect levels, and they can end up with a range of energies in the valence band.

Q What must be done to the artefact for this radiation to be emitted? [1]

A It must be heated.

Thermoluminescent dating techniques used on one stone artefact found in Australia suggest that humans lived there 50 000 years ago.

Q A similar-sized stone artefact found in another site emitted twice as much light. Estimate when this was last used by humans. [1]

A 100 000 years ago.

If the artefact has been exposed to radiation for twice as long, there will be twice as many electrons in defect levels and so twice as much light can be given out when they lose their energy.

Q State one assumption made in this estimate. [1]

A Each stone has been exposed to the same rate of radiation.

or The time each stone was last used by humans was the last time it was heated.

The question asks for just one assumption. The examiners would accept any one valid answer.

Photoelectric effect
DIG Section 3.4

When a single *photon* is absorbed by a metal surface its energy is transferred to a single electron, which may then be emitted from the metal. This process is called **photoelectric emission** and the emitted electron is known as a **photoelectron**.

The work function

The minimum energy required to release the electron is called the **work function** ϕ of the metal. For photoelectric emission to occur, the energy of the photon must be equal to or greater than the work function.

Photon energy equal to the work function

If the photon's energy E is *just* enough to release a photoelectron, then its frequency is called the **threshold frequency** f_0:

$$E = hf_0 = \phi$$

where h is the Planck constant (6.63×10^{-34} J s).

Photon energy greater than the work function

If the energy of the photon is greater than the work function, then the photoelectron can acquire some kinetic energy. By *energy conservation*:

photon energy = work done in releasing electron + kinetic energy of electron

In symbols this can be written in various ways, for example:

$$hf = \phi + E_{k\,max} \quad \text{or} \quad hf = hf_0 + E_{k\,max} \quad \text{or} \quad hf = \phi + \tfrac{1}{2}mv^2_{max}$$

where $E_{k\,max}$ ($= \tfrac{1}{2}mv^2_{max}$) is the maximum kinetic energy of the photoelectron. Electrons have less than the maximum kinetic energy if they transfer energy to the metal on their way to the surface.

Photon energy less than the work function

If the photon energy is *less* than the work function, the energy absorbed by the metal just causes a slight amount of heating.

Worked exam question

Q A photomultiplier which has a photocathode made from antimony–caesium has a threshold wavelength of 700 nm. Explain why a photocathode has a threshold wavelength.　　　　　　　　　　　　　　　　　　　　　　　　　　　　　　[4]

A An electron in the metal receives energy from a single photon. Photon energy $E = hf$. In order to leave the metal, an electron must receive energy equal to or greater than the work function ϕ of the metal. So there is a threshold frequency f_0 where $hf_0 = \phi$: radiation of any lower frequency will not eject the electron. The wavelength of the light is related to frequency $c = f\lambda$ so $\lambda_0 = c/f_0$. So λ_0 is the threshold wavelength: radiation with wavelength any *longer* than λ_0 will not eject an electron.

The question asks about wavelength, so be sure to include wavelength in your answer.

Q Show that the work function of antimony–caesium is about 3×10^{-19} J. [3]

A $\qquad \phi = hf_0 \quad$ and $\quad c = f\lambda, \quad$ so $\quad \phi = \dfrac{hc}{\lambda_0}$

$$\lambda_0 = 700 \text{ nm} = 700 \times 10^{-9} \text{ m}$$

$$\phi = \frac{3.00 \times 10^8 \text{ m s}^{-1} \times 6.63 \times 10^{-34} \text{ J s}}{700 \times 10^{-9} \text{ m}} = 2.84 \times 10^{-19} \text{ J}$$

- *The photoelectric equation is listed in the exam paper. Be careful: when $f = f_0$, the electron's kinetic energy $\frac{1}{2} mv^2 = 0$.*

- *700 nm is the wavelength, not the frequency. Express it in m to get an answer in SI units.*

- *In 'show that ...' questions, do the complete calculation and compare your answer with the one given.*

> Make sure you know the meanings of key terms and use them correctly.

✓ *Quick check 1–4*

? Quick check questions

1 The work function of barium is 4.00×10^{-19} J. What is its threshold frequency?

2 Blue light of frequency 7.06×10^{14} Hz is absorbed by barium. Calculate the maximum energy of the resulting photoelectrons.

3 Using the terms 'threshold frequency', 'photon energy', 'work function' and 'photoelectron', describe and explain what happens when red light of frequency 4.6×10^{14} Hz shines on barium.

4 For each of the following descriptions, say whether it refers to **A** a photon, **B** a photoelectron, **C** both, or **D** neither.

   a a 'packet' of light or other electromagnetic radiation

   b a small particle with negative charge

   c an electron that is ejected from a material when it absorbs radiation of sufficiently high frequency

   d can be created when something (e.g. an atom) loses energy, and ceases to exist when all its energy is absorbed.

Using straight-line graphs
DIG Section 3.4 and Maths Notes Sections 5.2 and 5.3

A relationship between two sets of physical quantities can be shown by a graph. If the graph is a straight line, then there is a *linear relationship* between the two quantities that can be expressed in an equation of the general form

$$y = mx + c$$

where y represents whatever is plotted on the y-axis and x represents whatever is plotted along the x-axis. The *gradient* of the graph is equal to the constant m and the *intercept on the y-axis* is equal to the *constant c*.

Graphs of experimental results

A straight-line graph of experimental measurements can be used to deduce the equation relating them. Finding values of the constants m and c from a best-fit graph is equivalent to carrying out separate calculations with each pair of experimental measurements and averaging the result.

Interpreting a graph

The graph shown is described by the equation

$$\tfrac{1}{2} mv^2_{max} = hf - hf_0$$

Here $\tfrac{1}{2} mv^2_{max}$ corresponds to y and f corresponds to x. Comparing this with $y = mx + c$, the gradient m corresponds to h.

The gradient of the graph can be used to find the Planck constant, h. Measure the rise of the graph, Δy, and the run, Δx.

$$h = \text{gradient } m = \frac{\Delta y}{\Delta x}$$

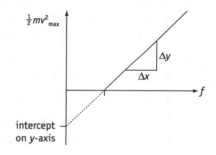

✓ Quick check 1

Drawing graphs

- When plotting a graph, make sure the scales are easy to plot and to read: use two, five or ten small squares for each interval of 1 or 0.1 on the axis.

- If you are going to use the graph to read off the intercept on the y-axis, make sure you start the x-axis at zero.

- Make the graph as big as possible: each axis should, if possible, cover at least half the length or width of the available paper.

- Plot the points carefully using a sharp pencil. If they lie close to a straight line, draw a best-fit line with a ruler.

Worked exam question

A thermometer is made for a piece of thin wire connected into a circuit that measures resistance. A student measures the resistance R over a range of temperatures θ. The graph below shows a line of best fit for the results.

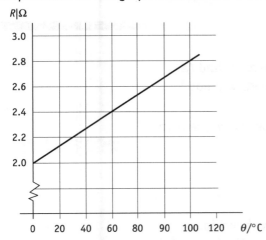

Q Use the graph to determine the equation of the line plotted. [4]

State the units for the gradient of this line. [1]

A The equation has the form $y = mx + c$, where y is R and x is θ. From the graph,

$$c = 2.0 \; \Omega$$

▶ The units of c are always the same as the units on the y-axis.

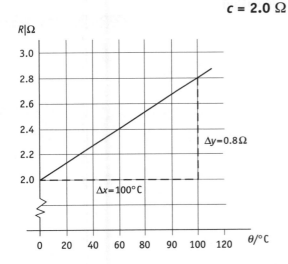

▶ To find the gradient, draw a large triangle using the whole of the best-fit line.

$$\text{gradient } m = \frac{\Delta y}{\Delta x} = \frac{0.8 \; \Omega}{100 \; °C} = 0.008 \; \Omega \; °C^{-1} = 8 \times 10^{-3} \; \Omega \; °C^{-1}$$

▶ The units of the gradient are always given by 'units on y-axis/units on x-axis'.

The equation is therefore

$$R = m\theta + c, \text{ where } m = 8 \times 10^{-3} \; \Omega \; °C^{-1} \text{ and } c = 2.0 \; \Omega$$

- *You could write $R = 8 \times 10^{-3} \; \Omega \; °C^{-1} \times \theta + 2.0 \; \Omega$. This is correct but clumsy. It is best to state the equation wholly in symbols accompanied by a clear statement of the values of m and c complete with their units.*

- *Be sure to use the symbols R and θ in your final answer, not y and x. If you wished, you could also use other symbols for the constants, reflecting the physical situation, e.g. $R = R_0 + k\theta$.*

? *Quick check question*

1 In the graph on page 46, what corresponds to the intercept on the y-axis?

Fluid flow

EAT Part 2

- **Laminar flow** is also called **streamlined flow**. It describes layers of fluid (a liquid or a gas), known as streamlines, flowing at different speeds and not crossing each other's paths.
- **Turbulent flow** describes layers of fluid flowing at different speeds, whose paths cross, mix and form vortices.

✓ *Quick check 1*

Viscosity

The **viscosity** of a fluid is a measure of the difficulty associated with moving adjacent layers of the fluid past each other. The lower the viscosity, the 'runnier' the fluid. The *rate of flow of a fluid depends*, among other things, upon the fluid's viscosity. If the fluid flow is laminar, then the flow rate decreases as viscosity increases. If the flow is turbulent, predictions of flow rate become difficult if not impossible. The viscosity of most fluids tends to decrease with increasing *temperature*.

✓ *Quick check 2*

Density

Density is mass per unit volume and is defined by

$$\rho = \frac{m}{V}$$

where ρ is **density**, m the mass and V the volume of an object.

Density has SI units kilograms per cubic metre, kg m^{-3}.

Upthrust

Upthrust is the *force* acting on a body fully or partially immersed in a fluid. It acts vertically upwards on the body. The magnitude of the upthrust U is equal to the weight of the fluid displaced by the body.

$$U = \rho Vg$$

where ρ = density of fluid, V = volume of body immersed in fluid, and g = gravitational field strength.

Viscous drag

Viscous drag is the *force* that opposes the motion of a body through a fluid, or the motion of a fluid through a pipe or around an object. The magnitude of the viscous drag acting on a body depends on the viscosity of the fluid, the size and shape of the body and its speed relative to the fluid.

✓ *Quick check 3*

Terminal velocity

Terminal velocity is the maximum velocity that a body reaches when moving through a fluid. As a body accelerates from rest, the viscous drag force increases until it balances any forces acting in the direction of motion. The *resultant force* on the body is now zero and its velocity does not change.

✓ *Quick check 4*

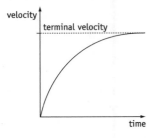

Stokes' Law

Stokes' Law describes the drag force F on a sphere moving through a fluid if the flow around the sphere is laminar:

$$F = 6\pi\eta r v$$

where η = viscosity of fluid, r = radius of sphere and v = velocity of sphere. The viscosity has SI units N s m^{-2}.

If a sphere is falling through a fluid at terminal velocity v_T, then the combined drag and upthrust, acting upwards, must exactly balance its weight:

$$6\pi\eta r v_T + U = mg$$

✓ *Quick check 5, 6*

Worked exam question

Some people think that all raindrops fall at the same speed; others think that their speed depends on their size.

Q Calculate the speed of a raindrop after it has fallen freely from rest for 0.2 s. [1]

A **Speed $v = u + at$** where $v = 0$, $t = 0.2$ s, $g = 9.81$ m s^{-2}

$v = 0.2$ s $\times$ 9.81 m s^{-2} = 1.96 m s^{-1} (= 2.0 m s^{-1} to 2 s.f.)

You sometimes need PSA1 work in PSA2, e.g. motion in free fall. You are expected to remember the relationship between acceleration, change in speed and time taken.

Q The raindrop falls for longer than 0.2 s. Explain why its acceleration does not remain uniform for the whole of its fall. [2]

A The drop's *motion through the air* gives rise to a *viscous drag force* which acts in the opposite direction to the drop's motion, *reducing the net downward force* on the drop. The *size of the drag force increases with the speed* of the drop, so the net downward force decreases and hence the *acceleration decreases*.

▶ This is a very thorough answer. Key points are in italics.

Q Show that the mass of a 0.5 mm diameter raindrop is less than 1×10^{-7} kg. 1.0 m³ of water has a mass of 1.0×10^3 kg. [2]

A
$$V = \frac{4\pi r^3}{3} \quad \text{and} \quad \rho = \frac{m}{V} \quad \text{so} \quad m = \rho V = \rho \times \frac{4\pi r^3}{3}$$

$$r = 0.25 \text{ mm} = 0.25 \times 10^{-3} \text{ m}, \rho = 1.0 \times 10^3 \text{ kg m}^{-3}$$

$$m = 1.0 \times 10^3 \text{ kg m}^{-3} \times \frac{4\pi}{3} \times (0.25 \times 10^{-3} \text{ m})^3$$

$$= 6.545 \times 10^{-8} \text{ kg}$$

which is less than 10^{-7} kg.

- *The formula for the volume of a sphere is listed in the exam paper. Make sure you are familiar with the list.*
- *Halve the diameter to find the radius, then express it in m to get the volume in m³.*
- *Do the algebra before putting in numbers.*
- *In 'show that ...' questions, do the complete calculation then compare your answer with the one given. If your own answer is very different, check your working.*

Q Calculate the raindrop's terminal velocity. Assume the upthrust from the air is negligible. Explain your working clearly. Viscosity of air = 1.8×10^{-5} kg m^{-1} s^{-1} [3]

A When $v = v_T$, net force = 0 so $mg = 6\pi\eta r v_T$ and

$$v_T = \frac{mg}{6\pi\eta r}$$

$$= \frac{6.545 \times 10^{-8} \text{ kg} \times 9.81 \text{ m s}^{-2}}{6\pi \times 1.8 \times 10^{-5} \text{ kg m}^{-1} \text{ s}^{-1} \times 0.25 \times 10^{-3} \text{ m}}$$

$$= 7.6 \text{ m s}^{-1}$$

- *The formula for viscous drag force is listed in the exam paper.*
- *If you got stuck doing the mass calculation earlier, use 1×10^{-7} kg.*

Q Sketch a graph to show how the raindrop's velocity increases from rest to terminal velocity. Add a scale to the vertical axis. [3]

A

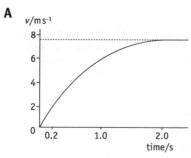

The gradient of the graph indicates acceleration. If the drop fell freely, the graph would be a straight line. Drag increases with speed so the gradient becomes less steep. When the drop reaches terminal velocity, the graph becomes horizontal (no acceleration).

Q Explain how the terminal velocity would be different for a larger raindrop.   [1]

A From earlier,
$$v_T = \frac{mg}{6\pi\eta r}$$

As $m = \rho V$ and $V = 4\pi r^3/3$,

$$v_T = \frac{4\pi r^3 \rho g}{18\pi\eta r} = \frac{2r^2 \rho g}{9\eta}$$

Therefore v_T is proportional to r^2 and so the larger the radius, the greater the terminal velocity.

This is a good answer, combining algebra with an explanation in words. A well-argued verbal answer would reach the same correct conclusion, though might be long-winded like the example below.

A A larger drop experiences a larger drag force at a given speed, but it also has a larger weight. The increasing weight 'wins', e.g. doubling the radius doubles the drag force but the volume and hence the weight are multiplied by 8. At any given speed, the drag is a smaller fraction of the weight and so the drop has to move faster before acceleration becomes zero. So terminal velocity is higher for larger drops.

? Quick check questions

1 Which diagram shows laminar flow and which shows turbulent flow?

(a)

(b)

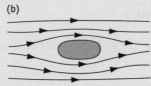

▶ Practise sketching these diagrams from memory.

2 Using the term 'viscosity', write a sentence to compare warm and cold syrup flowing from a spoon.

3 For each of the following, say whether it applies to **A** upthrust, **B** viscous drag, **C** both, or **D** neither.

 a has SI unit of newtons (N)

 b always acts upwards

 c can act in the absence of fluid

 d depends on relative speed of body and fluid

 e depends on size of body

 f depends on shape of body.

4 The figure on the right shows a skydiver falling with terminal velocity. The upthrust is very small and can be ignored. Add a labelled arrow to show the viscous drag force.

5 In what conditions can you ignore the upthrust on an object in a fluid?

6 Given the volume V of a sphere radius r is $V = 4\pi r^3/3$, use the equations on pages 48 and 49 to derive an expression for the terminal velocity of a sphere with density ρ_s, falling through a fluid of density ρ_f and viscosity η.

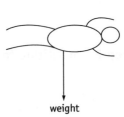

weight

Refraction

EAT Section 4.1

When waves (e.g. light or sound) meet a boundary between two materials, some of the beam is *reflected* and some is *refracted*, changing speed and direction. The **refractive index**, μ, for a pair of materials is the ratio of the wave velocities in the two materials. In the figure, the light ray is travelling from material 1 into material 2. The angles $\hat{1}$ and $\hat{2}$ are measured between the ray and the *normal* to the interface. Material 1 is less dense than material 2, and the speed of light is greater in material 1.

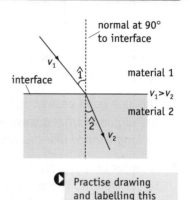

$$_1\mu_2 = \frac{v_1}{v_2}$$

$$= \frac{\text{sine of angle in material 1}}{\text{sine of angle in material 2}}$$

We often talk about *the* refractive index of a material. To be precise we should state the refractive index for a ray of light travelling from air (or vacuum) into the material. Hence μ for a material is in fact $_{air}\mu_{material}$. So we often see

$$\mu = \frac{\sin i}{\sin r}$$

where i is the angle of incidence in material 1 (air) and r is the angle of refraction in material 2.

Worked example

The refractive index of glass is 1.50 and that of water is 1.30. Calculate the refractive index *from water to glass*.

Step 1 Express refractive indices in terms of velocities:

$$_a\mu_g = \frac{v_a}{v_g} \quad \text{and} \quad _a\mu_w = \frac{v_a}{v_w}$$

where v_a is the velocity of light in air, v_w the velocity of light in water and v_g the velocity of light in glass.

$$_w\mu_g = \frac{v_w}{v_g}$$

Step 2 Substitute for v_w and v_g:

$$\frac{v_w}{v_g} = \frac{(v_a / _a\mu_w)}{(v_a / _a\mu_g)} = \frac{v_a}{_a\mu_w} \times \frac{_a\mu_g}{v_a}$$

$$\text{so } _w\mu_g = \frac{_a\mu_g}{_a\mu_w} = \frac{1.50}{1.30} = 1.15$$

normal at 90° to interface

Practise drawing and labelling this diagram from memory.

✓ *Quick check 1*

Total internal reflection

Total internal reflection occurs when the radiation cannot cross the interface between two materials but is reflected back into the first material. For light, it can occur only when a ray is travelling from a *more dense* to a *less dense* material, e.g. from water into air or from glass into air.

Critical angle

For total internal reflection, the angle of incidence within the denser material must be greater than a certain angle called the **critical angle** C.

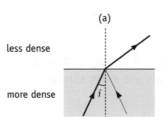 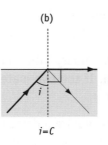 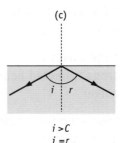

(a) *i* < C Most of the light emerges into the less dense material. A small fraction is internally reflected.

(b) *i* = C No light can emerge into the second material. It is refracted along the interface. Some light is internally reflected.

(c) *i* > C All the light is internally reflected – total internal reflection.

✓ *Quick check 2*

Critical angle is related to refractive index. From part (b) of the figure above and the illustration of refractive index on the opposite page,

$$_1\mu_2 = \frac{v_1}{v_2} = \frac{\sin 90°}{\sin C}$$

$$\sin 90° = 1 \quad \text{SO} \quad _1\mu_2 = \frac{1}{\sin C}$$

Worked example

Given that the speed of light in glass is 2.00×10^8 m s^{-1} and the speed of light in water is 2.25×10^8 m s^{-1}, calculate the critical angle for light travelling from glass to water.

Substitute values in the equation:

$$_w\mu_g = \frac{\sin C}{\sin 90°} = \frac{2.00 \times 10^8 \text{ m s}^{-1}}{2.25 \times 10^8 \text{ m s}^{-1}}$$

$$\sin C = 0.888 \quad \text{SO} \quad C = 62.7°$$

✓ *Quick check 3*

? *Quick check questions*

1 In the Worked example on page 52, what is the refractive index *from glass to water*?

2 Draw a diagram to show what happens to a ray of light travelling very close to an interface with a denser material, at an angle *very slightly* less than 90° with the normal.

3 Using the terms *refractive index, normal, critical angle* and *total internal reflection*, and other suitable terms, describe in detail what happens when a ray of light travels through water and reaches an air–water interface.

Pulse-echo techniques

SUR Part 4

Pulse-echo techniques use reflection of waves to detect the position and/or the motion of a boundary between two materials.

If the waves cross a boundary into a material of very different density, there is a strong reflected beam. If the two materials are more similar, the reflected beam is weaker.

Pulse echo techniques require a device which can generate and detect a short pulse of waves. Radar is a pulse-echo technique that uses radio waves. Medical ultrasound scanning is a pulse-echo technique using high-frequency sound waves.

The Doppler effect

When waves are emitted from a moving source, or detected with a moving receiver, the detected frequency differs from the emitted frequency. This is the **Doppler effect**.

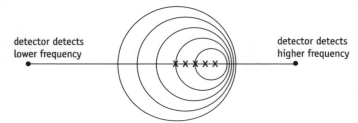

detector detects
lower frequency

detector detects
higher frequency

If the source and detector are stationary the detected frequency is the same as the emitted frequency. If the source and receiver are becoming closer together the detected frequency increases. If they are getting further apart, the detected frequency decreases. The amount by which the frequency is shifted depends on the speed of the motion.

Worked exam question

A sonar device, used on the surface of the sea, emits ultrasound waves of frequency 120 kHz to investigate the sea floor at a depth of 600 m. It maps the sea floor by measuring the time taken for the pulsed beam to return to the device.

Q The velocity of sound in sea water is 1500 m s^{-1}. Calculate the time between sending and receiving a pulse. [2]

A
$$\text{time} = \frac{\text{distance}}{\text{velocity}} = \frac{2 \times 600 \text{ m}}{1500 \text{ m s}^{-1}} = 0.80 \text{ s}$$

Take care. The pulse travels there and back, i.e. through twice the source–reflector distance.

Q No object can be detected by ultrasound if its dimensions are smaller than the wavelength of the signal. Calculate the size of the smallest object that can be detected with this system. [2]

> ❶ You are expected to know the relationship between distance, velocity and time.

A

$$v = f\lambda \quad \text{so} \quad \lambda = \frac{v}{f}$$

$$\lambda = \frac{1500 \text{ m s}^{-1}}{120 \times 10^3 \text{ Hz}} = 1.25 \times 10^{-2} \text{ m}$$

Q State, with reasons, whether you could recognise a wrecked ship on the sea floor using this sonar device. [1]

A Yes. A wreck would be much larger than the wavelength.

A diver leaves the wreck to come to the boat. The sonar signal is reflected from the moving diver with a different frequency from the transmitted signal.

Q What is the name of this effect? What information does the change in frequency give you about the diver? [2]

A Doppler effect. The speed of the diver towards/away from the boat.

Q Sonar devices emit high-intensity ultrasound. Suggest an *environmental* problem which the use of sonar might pose. [1]

A It could confuse dolphins that use ultrasound for communication.

or It could deafen sea creatures.

or any reasonable suggestion.

Examiners would give credit for any reasonable answer related to the question, but they would not give marks for vague answers such as 'might harm animals'.

> You are expected to know the relationship between frequency, velocity and wavelength.

✓ *Quick check 1*

? **Quick check question**

1 Using the terms *reflection*, *Doppler shift* and other suitable terms, explain how it is possible for a pulse-echo technique to detect the position, size and speed of an object.

Lenses

SUR Section 3.2

A *lens* refracts radiation (usually light) and can form an image.

- A *real image* is one through which rays of light actually pass, and so can be formed on a screen.

- A *virtual image* is one that light rays only *seem* to come from.

Lens formula

For a thin lens:

$$\frac{1}{u} + \frac{1}{v} = \frac{1}{f}$$

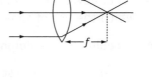

f is positive

where *u* is the object distance, *v* the image distance and *f* the focal length of the lens. All distances are measured from the centre of the lens.

In this equation distances to real objects and images are positive, and virtual distances are negative. A *converging* lens has a positive focal length and a *diverging* lens has a negative focal length.

f is negative

Worked example

A diverging lens has focal length 20 cm. It is placed 30 cm from an object. What is the distance of the image? Is it real or virtual?

Step 1   Write down what you know, and what you want to know:

$$f = -20 \text{ cm}, \ u = 30 \text{ cm}, \ v = ?$$

Step 2   Rearrange the lens formula and substitute values:

$$\frac{1}{v} = \frac{1}{f} - \frac{1}{u} = -\frac{1}{20 \text{ cm}} - \frac{1}{30 \text{ cm}} = -0.05 \text{ cm}^{-1} - 0.033 \text{ cm}^{-1} = -0.083 \text{ cm}^{-1}$$

$$v = -\frac{1}{0.083 \text{ cm}^{-1}} = -12 \text{ cm}$$

The image is 12 cm from the lens. It is virtual (*v* is negative).

 ✓ *Quick check 1*

Worked exam question

At the theatre, people in the audience sometimes use theatre glasses. These are special binoculars which help them to see the actors. For each eye, the lenses in the theatre glasses are arranged as shown.

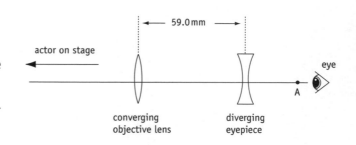

An actor is standing on a stage 30 m from a member of the audience who is using the glasses. The objective lens has focal length 80 mm and forms an image of the actor 80 mm behind this lens at A.

Q Calculate the power of the objective lens. [1]

A
$$f = 80 \times 10^{-3} \text{ m}$$

$$P = \frac{1}{f} = \frac{1}{80 \times 10^{-3} \text{ m}} = 12.5 \text{ D}$$

> To get the power in dioptres, the focal length must be in metres.

The eyepiece is a diverging lens of focal length 20.0 mm. The image at A formed by the objective lens acts as the object for the eyepiece. The final position of the image formed by the eyepiece can be calculated using

$$\frac{1}{v} - \frac{1}{21 \text{ mm}} = \frac{1}{f}$$

Q Suggest why the object distance is negative. [1]

A The rays of light never actually reach A, so it acts as a 'virtual object'.

You are not expected to have met this situation before, so the question asks you to 'suggest ...'. In such questions you are expected to make a sensible suggestion based on your knowledge and understanding of physics.

Q Calculate the final position of the image formed by the eyepiece. [2]

A
$$\frac{1}{v} = \frac{1}{f} - \left(-\frac{1}{21 \text{ mm}} \right)$$

For the eyepiece, $f = -20$ mm, so

$$\frac{1}{v} = -\frac{1}{20 \text{ mm}} + \frac{1}{21 \text{ mm}} = -0.0024 \text{ mm}^{-1}$$

$$v = \frac{1}{0.0024 \text{ mm}^{-1}} = -420 \text{ mm}$$

- *Keep all the distances in mm. You could convert to m, but that would make the numbers clumsier.*
- *Be very careful with signs and with handling reciprocals.*

Q Is the image real or virtual? Explain your answer. [1]

A Virtual, as v is a negative distance. The rays of light do not actually pass through the image.

? ## Quick check question

1 A diverging lens of focal length 50 cm forms a virtual image 25 cm from the lens. Where is the object?

Polarisation

EAT Section 4.2

Light is a *transverse wave*. It consists of varying electric and magnetic fields at right angles to its direction of motion.

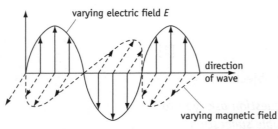

▶ Practise sketching this diagram from memory.

- In **plane polarised light**, often called simply *polarised light*, the variations in electric field strength take place *only in the plane of polarisation*; there are magnetic variations in the plane at right angles to this.

- In *unpolarised light* these variations take place in all planes containing the direction in which the wave is travelling.

Longitudinal waves, such as sound waves, cannot be plane polarised.

Polarising filter

▶ Practise sketching this diagram from memory.

- If unpolarised light encounters a polarising filter (Polaroid) some of it is absorbed and the emerging light is polarised.

- If polarised light encounters a polarising filter, polarised light emerges whose brightness and plane of polarisation depends on the orientation of the filter.

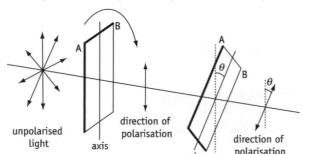

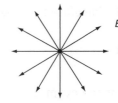

Optical activity

Optically active substances, such as sugar solutions, *rotate* the plane of polarisation by an amount proportional to their *concentration* and the depth through which the light travels. This effect is used by the food industry to measure the concentration of sugar solutions.

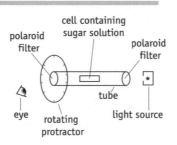

✓ *Quick check 1*

Worked exam question

A photographer uses a polarising filter over the camera lens. She notices that the intensity of the light received from the blue sky changes as she rotates the filter.

Q What does this suggest about light from the sky? [1]

A The light is polarised.

Q Explain the changes in intensity as the filter is rotated. [2]

A The filter allows through light that is polarised in one direction (one plane) only. When the filter is aligned with the direction of polarisation, light travels through it. When it is at 90° to the direction of polarisation, no polarised light gets through.

This answer would be greatly enhanced by diagrams like those on the opposite page. If there is space available, include diagrams where they help your answer – even if the question does not ask for them.

The use of a polarising filter makes a blue sky appear darker, but the clouds remain bright.

Q Suggest a reason why there is little change in the intensity of the light from the clouds. [1]

A The light must be unpolarised.

Polarisation is the key point here. The colours of the sky and clouds are irrelevant.

Astronomers notice the same effect with the radio waves emitted by some galaxies.

Q What does this suggest about these radio waves? [1]

A The waves are polarised.

When a question asks you to 'suggest ...', you are expected to make a sensible suggestion based on your knowledge and understanding of physics.

Q State why radio waves should behave in the same way as light waves. [1]

A Light and radio waves are both electromagnetic radiation. They are transverse waves so can be polarised.

❓ *Quick check question*

1 Summarise the steps involved in calibrating a polarimeter using sugar solutions of known concentration, then using it to find the sugar concentration of a solution with unknown concentration.

Properties of materials
EAT Part 3

- **Elastic deformation** describes a change in shape of a material which is not permanent. When the deforming load is removed the material returns to its original shape.

- **Plastic deformation** is permanent. When the deforming load is removed the material does not return to its original shape.

- **Brittle** describes a material that breaks without suffering plastic deformation, e.g. cast iron, wafer biscuit.

- **Ductile** materials easily undergo plastic deformation by being pulled into wires or strings, e.g. copper, soft chewing-gum.

- **Malleable** materials easily undergo plastic deformation by being hammered or rolled into shape, e.g. soft iron, uncooked pastry.

- **Hard** describes a material that resists surface indentation, e.g. chromium, boiled sweet.

- **Stiff** describes a material that suffers little deformation (either plastic or elastic) even when subjected to large loads, e.g. high tensile steel.

- **Tough** describes a material that can absorb a lot of energy and undergo large plastic deformation without breaking. Tough materials are able to absorb the energy of a sudden impact, e.g. 0.8% carbon steel, toffee (the sort that sticks your teeth together).

✓ *Quick check 1*

▶ To clarify the meanings of these terms, try to think of an object or a material that has one property but not another. For example, 'hard' is not the same as 'brittle': a wafer biscuit is brittle (it snaps without deforming) but not hard (you can easily bite into it).

✓ *Quick check 2*

❓ Quick check questions

1 Which of the graphs here shows 'elastic deformation' and which shows 'plastic deformation'?

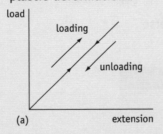
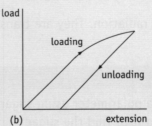

2 Suggest objects or materials that illustrate the difference between 'hard' and 'tough'.

Energy in stretching a sample
SUR Section 2.2

The **elastic strain energy** E_{el} is the energy stored in a sample that has not reached its elastic limit and is equal to the work done in stretching or compressing it. The work done in deforming any sample is equal to the *area under the force–extension or force–compression graph*.

If the graph is a *straight line through the origin*, the area is a triangle and

$$E_{el} = \tfrac{1}{2}\, Fx$$

If the graph is not a straight line, the area must be found by *counting squares* under the line.

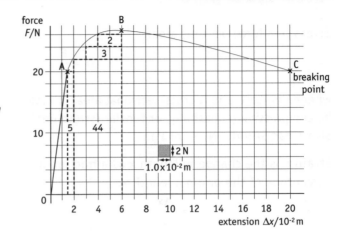

Worked examples

1   What is the energy stored in the sample when it is stretched as far as point A in the figure above?

At A, $F = 20$ N, extension $x = 1.5 \times 10^{-2}$ m

$$E_{el} = \frac{20\ \text{N} \times 1.5 \times 10^{-2}\ \text{m}}{2} = 0.15\ \text{J}$$

> Take care reading the units of x from the graph.
> $x/10^{-2}$ m = 1.5
> so $x = 1.5 \times 10^{-2}$ m.

2   What is the work done in stretching the wire from point A to point B? What is the total work done in stretching the wire by 6×10^{-2} m?

The small shaded square represents $2\ \text{N} \times 1.0 \times 10^{-2}$ m, i.e. 2.0×10^{-2} J. Under the graph between A and B there are between 56 and 57 such squares. If we say 56, then the work done is:

$$56 \times 2.0 \times 10^{-2}\ \text{J} = 1.12\ \text{J}$$

total work done = 1.12 J + 0.15 J = 1.27 J (= 1.3 J to 2 s.f.)

- *This part must be done by counting squares as the graph is not a straight line.*

- *It is often difficult to estimate fractions of squares from a graph so it is best to find the nearest whole number. Examiners generally allow a range of answers.*

- *The final answer can be rounded as it is not very precise.*

✓ *Quick check 1*

❓ Quick check question

1   What is the total work done in breaking the wire shown in the figure above?

Materials under stress

SUR Section 2.2

Stress σ is force per unit area.

$$\sigma = \frac{F}{A}$$

where F is force and A cross-sectional area. It may be compressive (squashing) or tensile (stretching). Stress has SI units N m^{-2} or Pa.

Strain ε is the change in length x as a fraction or percentage of the original length x.

$$\varepsilon = \frac{\Delta x}{x}$$

Strain can be tensile or compressive. It is a ratio and so has no units.

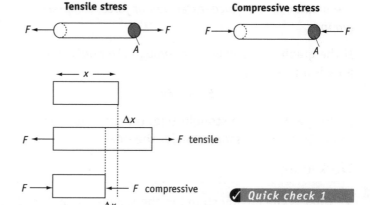

✓ *Quick check 1*

Worked examples

1 A wire of diameter 1.2 mm is stretched by a force of 25 N. What is the stress in the wire?

Step 1 Find the cross-sectional area:

$$r = 0.6 \text{ mm} = 0.6 \times 10^{-3} \text{ m} \quad \text{so} \quad A = \pi r^2 = \pi \times (0.6 \times 10^{-3} \text{ m})^2$$

▶ Halve the diameter to get the radius, and express it in m so that you get the area in m².

Step 2 Write down the equation, substitute and solve:

$$\sigma = \frac{F}{A} = \frac{25 \text{ N}}{\pi \times (0.6 \times 10^{-3} \text{ m})^2} = 2.2 \times 10^7 \text{ N m}^{-2}$$

This stress could also be written as 2.2×10^7 Pa or 22 MPa, where 1 MPa = 10^6 Pa.

✓ *Quick check 2*

2 A sample of bone is 10 cm long. It is then compressed by 0.5 mm. What is the strain?

Step 1 Convert units to m:

$$\Delta x = 0.5 \text{ mm} = 0.5 \times 10^{-3} \text{ m} \quad \text{and} \quad x = 0.1 \text{ m}$$

▶ You must express x and Δx in the *same units*. The strain can be expressed either as a fraction or a percentage.

Step 2 Write down the equation, substitute and solve:

$$\varepsilon = \frac{\Delta x}{x} = \frac{0.5 \times 10^{-3} \text{ m}}{0.1 \text{ m}} = 5 \times 10^{-3} = 0.005 = 0.5\%$$

✓ *Quick check 3*

Strength and stiffness

A **strong** material is one that can withstand stress without breaking or plastic deformation. A **stiff** material is one that undergoes little strain when placed under stress.

Stress–strain graphs

The mechanical properties of a *sample* can be shown on a graph of force against extension or compression. A graph of stress against strain shows the properties of a *material*. *All* samples of the same material have the same stress–strain graph.

This figure illustrates terms used to describe material behaviour. Not all materials show the full range of behaviour – some fail without reaching point C.

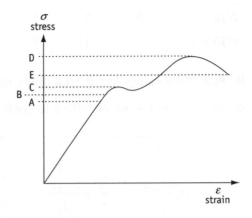

- The **limit of proportionality** (A): the stress up to which stress is directly proportional to strain.
- The **elastic limit** (B): the stress up to which the material returns to its original dimensions when the load is removed.
- The **yield point** (C): the stress beyond which plastic deformation occurs.
- The **ultimate tensile stress** (D): the maximum stress the material can withstand.
- The **breaking stress** (E): the stress at which the material breaks. For many materials, this is the same as (D), but in this figure the sample continues to extend, even when the load is reduced.

Note that these are all values of *stress*.

Practise sketching and labelling this diagram from memory.

The Young modulus

For *stresses up to the limit of proportionality*, the behaviour of materials is often described in terms of their **Young modulus**, *E*.

$$E = \frac{\text{stress}}{\text{strain}} = \frac{\sigma}{\varepsilon}$$

The SI units of *E* are the same as the units of stress, N m^{-2}.

Worked example

A wire, 1.5 m long, is subjected to a tensile stress of 2.1×10^8 Pa which produces an extension of 2.5 mm. What is the strain? What is the Young modulus of the material?

Step 1 Find the strain:

$$\varepsilon = \frac{2.5 \times 10^{-3} \text{ m}}{1.5 \text{ m}} = 1.7 \times 10^{-3}$$

Step 2 Write down the equation, substitute and solve:

$$E = \frac{\sigma}{\varepsilon} = \frac{2.1 \times 10^8 \text{ Pa}}{1.7 \times 10^{-3}} = 1.2 \times 10^{11} \text{ Pa}$$

In calculations involving the Young modulus, strain *must* be expressed as a fraction (decimal), not as a percentage.

✓ *Quick check 4–6*

Worked exam question

Control of high volume manufacturing production, such as in the steel industry, is achieved through regular sampling and testing of the product. In one test, a rod of steel approximately the size of a pencil is subjected to an increasing stress.

The results below were from a test on a sample of steel 1.3×10^{-4} m^2 cross-sectional area and 6.5×10^{-2} m length. The tension T applied to the sample and its resulting extension x were measured until the sample failed.

$T/10^3$ N	0	5	10	15	20	25	30	35
$x/10^{-6}$ m	0	12	24	36	48	60	74	100

Q Plot these values and draw a graph on the grid below. [3]

Q Indicate on the graph with a letter P the limit of proportionality. [1]

A

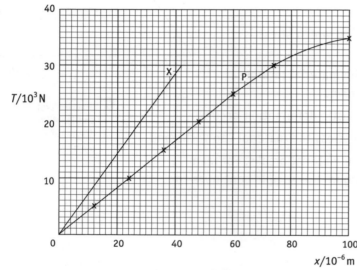

- *Graphs of force against extension are usually plotted with force on the y-axis.*
- *Choose a scale that is easy to plot and to read, and that occupies at least half the length and width of the graph paper.*
- *Label the axes clearly, including units.*
- *Plot the points carefully, using a sharp pencil. Where they lie on a straight line, draw a line through them with a ruler.*
- *Make sure point P is clearly marked. It is the point where the graph curves away from a straight line. It must lie somewhere between the readings for T = 25 and 30×10^3 N.*

Q Calculate the stress applied to the specimen at this point. [2]

A Taking P as the point where $T = 25 \times 10^3$ N, $x = 60 \times 10^{-6}$ m.

$$\textbf{stress} = \frac{\textbf{force}}{\textbf{area}} = \frac{\textbf{25} \times \textbf{10}^3 \textbf{ N}}{\textbf{1.3} \times \textbf{10}^{-4} \textbf{ m}^2} = \textbf{1.9} \times \textbf{10}^8 \textbf{ N m}^{-2} \textbf{ (or Pa)}$$

- *If you extended the straight line beyond 25×10^3 N your calculation would use a slightly higher value of T. The examiners would accept a range of answers depending on exactly where you ended the straight line on your graph.*

- *Take care with units and powers of ten. Make sure you know how to read them from the table and the graph. For example if $T/10^3$ N = 25, then $T = 25 \times 10^3$ N.*

Q Calculate the strain in the sample at P. [1]

A Again taking P as the point where $T = 25 \times 10^3$ N, $x = 60 \times 10^{-6}$ m.

$$\textbf{strain} = \frac{\textbf{extension}}{\textbf{original length}} = \frac{60 \times 10^{-6} \textbf{ m}}{6.5 \times 10^{-2} \textbf{ m}} = 9.2 \times 10^{-4}$$

> **◖** Remember strain has no units.

As with the stress calculation, examiners allow a range of values depending on the position of P on your graph.

Q Calculate the Young modulus for this steel. [1]

A   **Young modulus** $= \dfrac{\textbf{stress}}{\textbf{strain}} = \dfrac{\textbf{1.9} \times \textbf{10}^8 \textbf{ N m}^{-2}}{\textbf{9.2} \times \textbf{10}^{-4}} = \textbf{2.1} \times \textbf{10}^{11} \textbf{ N m}^{-2} \textbf{ (or Pa)}$

Even if your point P is further along the graph, you should still get exactly the same answer for this calculation as P lies on a straight line through the origin.

A second sample of exactly the same size is stiffer, weaker and brittle.

Q Sketch a line on your graph predicting the result for the sample. Label this line X. [2]

A See graph.

The line must be steeper because the sample is stiffer, and end at a tension less than 25×10^3 N because the sample is weaker. It does not curve, because the sample is brittle and so does not deform plastically.

? *Quick check questions*

1 What are the SI units of **a** stress, **b** strain?

2 What force needs to be applied to a sample 3.0 mm in diameter to produce a stress of 3.5×10^8 Pa?

3 A sample 1.2 m long experiences a strain of 0.25%. By how much does it extend?

4 Which of the graphs shown on the right is for a brittle material?

5 Write an equation for E in terms of F, A, x and Δx.

6 A stress of 70 MPa strains a glass fibre by 0.1%. What is the Young modulus of the glass?

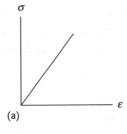

(a)

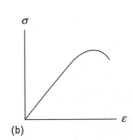

(b)

X-rays and diffraction
DIG Part 2

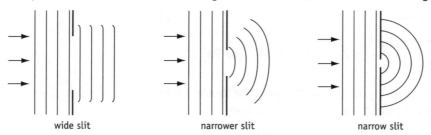

Diffraction is the *bending of wave fronts* as the wave passes through a *gap* or around an *obstacle*. The effect is most pronounced when the gap or obstacle is comparable in size to the wavelength of the wave, as shown in the figure.

wide slit	narrower slit	narrow slit

> Practise making accurate sketches of this figure from memory. Take care to draw the waves so that their wavelength is the same both before and after diffraction.

X-rays are *electromagnetic radiation* in the approximate wavelength range 10^{-11} to 10^{-8} m. They can be used to examine objects hidden from view (e.g. inside archaeological objects or human bodies) because they penetrate some materials that are opaque to visible light but are absorbed by others (including metals).

X-ray diffraction

X-ray *diffraction* is used to explore the arrangements of atoms within solid materials. As the X-rays travel through the material, they are diffracted. Superposition of the diffracted waves produces an interference pattern like that in the figure. The pattern depends on the nature of the atoms in the material and the way they are arranged; a regular arrangement of atoms gives rise to a clear pattern of bright diffracted beams, but a random arrangement scatters the X-rays more evenly.

✔ *Quick check 1*

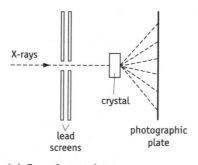

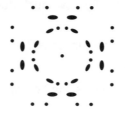

(a) Experimental set-up   (b) X-ray diffraction photograph

? *Quick check question*

1 Visible light ranges in wavelength from 4×10^{-7} m to 7×10^{-7} m. Explain why a beam of visible light passes straight through a transparent crystal (such as quartz) but the same crystal produces a diffraction pattern with X-rays.

Polymers and electron diffraction

SUR Section 2.3

Polymers are *long molecules*, usually based on chains of carbon atoms. Silicon can also form polymers. By controlling the chemical make-up of the molecules, their length and the way they are arranged, it is possible to engineer polymer materials to have a wide range of mechanical and optical properties.

Electron diffraction

When a beam of fast-moving *electrons* shines through a thin slice of material, it is diffracted. The electrons are *behaving like waves* rather than particles. The diffraction is most noticeable when the size of the *wavelength* associated with the electrons is comparable to the size and separation of the atoms.

Diffraction patterns

If the atoms are arranged regularly within the material, the diffracted electron beams emerge in a clear pattern, but a random arrangement of atoms scatters the beam of electrons more evenly.

Electron diffraction is an important technique for studying polymers and other materials made up of light atoms such as carbon. Electron beams are readily affected by light atoms, whereas X-rays are more affected by heavy atoms such as metals.

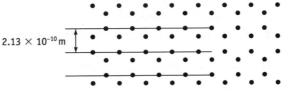

2.13 × 10⁻¹⁰ m

The figure shows the arrangement of carbon atoms in graphite. An electron beam is diffracted as it passes through a graphite sample then meets a phosphorescent screen, causing it to glow.

Worked example

1 State the *order of magnitude* of the electron wavelength.

The separation of the layers of atoms must be comparable to the wavelegnth of the electrons in order to produce noticeable diffraction. The separation of the layers is 2.13×10^{-10}, so the wavelength must be about 10^{-10} m.

> ▶ 'Order of magnitude' means 'size to the nearest power of ten'.
>
> ✓ *Quick check 1*

❓ *Quick check question*

1 Using the terms *diffraction*, *wavelength* and other suitable terms, explain how electrons can be used to study the structure of polymers.

Practice exam questions for PSA2

1 This diagram shows a strain gauge. The resistance of this device changes when it is deformed. It is used on bridges to monitor any changes such as flexing at the joints or extension of the supporting cables

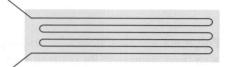

The strain gauge consists of a length of very fine wire, looped as shown, which has been cemented between two sheets of very thin paper. It is firmly glued to the surface that is to be monitored.

Explain why the resistance of the strain gauge changes when it is stretched.   [2]

Explain an advantage of using the arrangement of wire shown in the diagram. [1]

Draw a diagram showing a circuit you could use to measure the resistance of the strain gauge.   [2]

The wire used for the gauge is 0.20 m long and has a diameter of 2.0×10^{-4} m. Show that this wire has a resistance of about 3 Ω.

Resistivity = 4.9×10^{-7} Ω m.   [3]

From Edexcel June 2001, Unit PSA2   [Total: 8]

2 Opticians use a fluorescein test to check the eyes of people who wear contact lenses. A liquid dye (fluorescein) is put in the eyes. When blue light is shone on to the eyes the fluorescein absorbs this and emits a green light. Any damaged areas of the cornea show as brighter regions.

The maximum absorption of the blue light is at a frequency of 6.2×10^{14} Hz.

Calculate the energy in joules of an absorbed photon of this blue light.   [1]

The green light emitted by the fluorescein has a frequency less than that of the blue light absorbed.

Explain, with the help of an energy level diagram, what happens to an electron within the fluorescein as this liquid absorbs blue light and emits green light. [4]

In practice, the liquid dye absorbs and emits a narrow band of frequencies. Suggest an explanation for this.   [2]

From Edexcel January 2000, Unit PSA2   [Total: 7]

3 Albert Einstein is probably best known for his work on relativity but he also carried out important research into the absorption and emission of light from atoms. Einstein received the Nobel Prize in 1921 for his work on the photoelectric effect.

The Einstein photoelectric equation is written as

$$hf = \phi + \tfrac{1}{2}mv^2_{max}$$

Explain what the following two parts of this equation represent:

- hf

- ϕ [3]

State the SI unit of hf.   [1]

Why does the last term in the equation have the suffix 'max'?   [2]

From Edexcel June 2000, Unit PSA2   [Total: 6]

4 When oil is pumped round a car engine it is essential that it flows at the correct rate. It must coat the moving parts and still move quickly through narrow passages. To ensure that this happens the viscosity of the oil must be measured.

One way of measuring the coefficiency of viscosity is to use a falling ball viscometer. In this instrument a sphere is dropped into the liquid and its subsequent motion is recorded. This motion can be analysed in terms of the *viscous drag*, the upthrust and the weight of the sphere. Stokes' law can be used if the flow is *laminar*. When *terminal velocity* has been reached measurements can be made to determine the coefficient of viscosity.

Explain the meaning of the words in italics:

- viscous drag   [1]

- laminar flow   [1]

- terminal velocity   [2]

Draw a labelled diagram showing the forces acting on the sphere when it is falling at constant velocity.   [1]

The sphere has a radius r and it is made from a material of density ρ.
Write down an expression for the weight W of the sphere.   [1]

The sphere experiences an upthrust force $U = \tfrac{4}{3}\pi r^3 \sigma g$ where σ is the density of the oil.

Explain briefly the cause of the upthrust force on the sphere.   [1]

Explain why, when the sphere is falling with terminal velocity, $F = W - U$ where F is the Stokes' law force.   [1]

Hence show that the viscosity η can be calculated from the expression

$$\eta = \frac{2r^2 g(\rho - \sigma)}{9v}$$

where v is the velocity of the sphere. [2]

Explain why it is important that the experiment is performed using hot oil. [2]

From Edexcel June 1999, Unit PSA2 [Total: 12]

5 Farmers can choose the best time to harvest some fruits by measuring how much sugar their juice contains. The concentration of sugar in the juice alters its refractive index which can be measured with a refractometer. The figure to the right shows a beam of light entering a refractometer. The juice is placed on top of the prism.

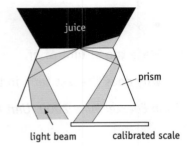

The light coming out of the prism hits the scale as shown in the figure. Explain why part of the scale appears dark. [2]

A student uses a prism to investigate this effect in the school laboratory. A layer of juice is trapped between the prism and a microscope slide. The figure below shows a ray of light hitting the surface between the prism and the juice at the critical angle.

Mark the following angles on the figure:

the critical angle C

an incident angle i

a refracted angle r [3]

Explain the term *critical angle*. [2]

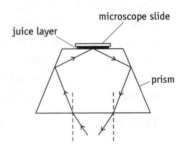

The student calculates these values of refractive index for different concentrations of sugar solution.

concentration of sugar solution/%	refractive index of sugar solution
0	1.333
15	1.356
30	1.381
45	1.410
60	1.442

Plot a graph of these results on the grid below. [4]

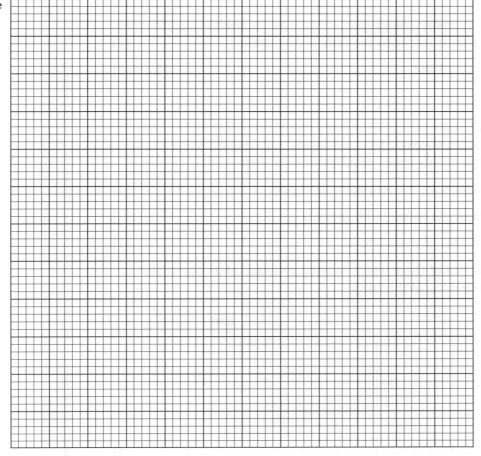

refractive
index

percentage concentration of sugar solution

From the graph, find the refractive index of a sugar solution of concentration
40%. [1]

From Edexcel January 2001, Unit PSA2 [Total: 12]

6 An ultrasound A-scan is a test that is commonly carried out to check that a fetus
is developing correctly and growing at the expected rate. A typical use would be
to monitor the growth of a baby's head.

The picture on the left and the simplified diagram on the right show a scan of the
baby's head.

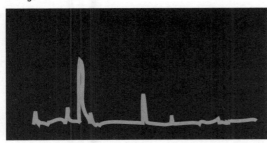

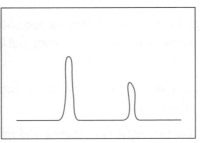

Trace seen on monitor   **Simplified diagram of trace**

What quantity is represented by the horizontal axis of the trace? [1]

Explain briefly how the two peaks of the trace are formed. [2]

Explain briefly how the trace could be used to obtain a measurement of the size of the baby's head. [3]

If ultrasound is used to image a moving object such as the heart, a Doppler shift is observed. Explain what is meant by the term *Doppler shift*. [2]

From Edexcel June 1999, Unit PSA2 [Total: 8]

7 A student is unable to focus on objects that are more than 2.0 m away unless he is wearing his glasses. His glasses enable him to see a distant object clearly by forming a virtual image of this object at 2.0 m from his eyes.

Explain whether the lenses are converging or diverging. [1]

State the focal length of the lenses in his glasses. [1]

Hence, calculate the power of these lenses. [1]

Draw a ray diagram of one of these lenses forming an image of an object that is 4.0 m away from the lens. Label the image.

[3]

During his next sight test, the optician finds that the student's sight has changed.

The student sees clearly when an additional lens of power +0.20 D is combined with his existing lens.

Calculate the power of this new lens combination. [1]

Explain whether the student's sight when not wearing glasses has improved or worsened. [1]

From Edexcel June 2001, Unit PSA2 [Total: 8]

8 Light reflected from the glass surface of a microscope slide can be plane polarised. Draw labelled diagrams to show how plane polarised light is different from ordinary light. [2]

The reflected light is best polarised when the angle of incidence is 57°. The angle of refraction in the glass is 33°.

Draw a diagram to show how this light is reflected and refracted at the surface of the microscope slide. On your diagram, mark the angles you know and draw an eye observing the plane polarised light. [3]

A polarising filter is placed in the path of the reflected beam of light. State what the observer sees as the polarising filter is rotated through 360°.   [2]

Explain these observations.   [2]

Calculate the refractive index of the glass used for the microscope slide.   [1]

From Edexcel January 2000, Unit PSA2   [Total: 10]

9 You have been asked to give a talk on materials to your physics class and have started to make a summary sheet of the materials you want to mention.

Complete the table.   [5]

property	explanation	example
brittle		glass
malleable		
stiff	large stress produces only small strain	
ductile		copper

From Edexcel June 2000, Unit PSA2   [Total: 5]

Answers to quick check questions

Unit PSA1

Motion equations and graphs

Page 3

1. $t = (v - u)/a$

2. Taking downwards as positive: $u = 0.0$ m s^{-1}, $t = 2.0$ s, $s = ?$, $a = g = 9.81$ m s^{-2}

   $s = ut + \frac{1}{2}at^2 = 0 + \frac{1}{2} \times 9.81$ m s$^{-2} \times (2.0$ s$)^2 =$ 19.6 m (= 20 m to 2 s.f.)

3. $u = 0.0$ m s^{-1}, $v = 5.0$ m s^{-1}, $s = 30$ m, $a = ?$

   $v^2 = u^2 + 2as$ so $2as = v^2 - u^2$ and $a = (v^2 - u^2)/2s$

   $a = (5.0$ m s$^{-1})^2/(2 \times 30$ m$) = 0.42$ m s^{-2}

4. The acceleration decreases steadily. A tangent drawn at the origin rises to about 5.0 m s^{-1} after 7.0 s, so initial acceleration $a = 5.0$ m s$^{-1}/7.0$ s $= 0.71$ m s^{-2}. (Your value will depend on exactly where you drew your line, but it should be close to ours.)

Force and acceleration

Page 5

1. SI units of g are m s^{-2} or N kg^{-1}.

2. **a** A, **b** B, **c** A, **d** C, **e** C, **f** C

3. Mass m = 24.5 tonne = 24.5 $\times$ 10^3 kg

   initial velocity u = 252 km h^{-1}

   = 252 $\times$ 10^3 m/3600 s = 70 m s^{-1}

   final velocity v = 0

   $v^2 = u^2 + 2as$ so $a = (v^2 - u^2)/2s = -(70$ m s$^{-1})^2/(2 \times 70$ m$) = -35$ m s^{-2}

   $F = ma = 24.5 \times 10^3$ kg $\times -35$ m s$^{-2} = -8.58 \times 10^5$ N

   The negative sign shows that the force acts against the direction of motion, as expected.

4. **a** $W = mg = 0.100$ kg $\times 9.81$ N kg$^{-1} = 0.981$ N

   b Net upward force = 1.5 N – 0.981 N = 0.52 N

Combining and resolving forces

Page 7

1. The force vector R has magnitude 16 N and acts at 22.5° to the 10.0 N force.

2. $R^2 = (36 + 100)$ N$^2 = 136$ N^2 so $R = 11.7$ N (12 N to 2 s.f.)

   $\tan \theta = \dfrac{6.0}{10.0} = 0.60$ so $\theta = 31°$

3. Horizontal component $F \cos 35° = 61.4$ N. Vertical component $F \sin 35° = 43.0$ N.

4. Resolving along the direction of the forcemeter and equating components:

   $2T \cos 55° = 15.0$ N so $T = 15.0/2 \cos 55° = 13.1$ N

5. Resolving vertically and equating components of forces acting at point A:

   $T \sin 35° = W = mg$, so $T = mg/\sin 35° =$ 0.500 kg $\times 9.81$ N kg$^{-1}/\sin 35° = 8.6$ N

   Resolving horizontally and equating components of forces acting at point A:

   $R = T \cos 35° = 8.6$ N cos 35° = 7.1 N

Energy, work and power

Page 9

1. $\Delta W = 12$ N $\times 0.80$ m = 9.6 J

2. Component of force along direction of motion:

   $F = 2 \times 50 \times 10^3$ N $\times \cos 20° = 9.4 \times 10^4$ N.

   Energy transferred = $F\Delta x = 9.4 \times 10^4$ N $\times 10$ m = 9.4×10^5 J.

3. $\Delta E_{grav} = mg\Delta h = 85$ kg $\times 9.81$ N kg$^{-1} \times 2.5 \times 10^3$ m = 2.1×10^6 J

4. Mass $m = 1.2 \times 10^3$ kg.

   $E_k = \frac{1}{2} \times 1.2 \times 10^3$ kg $\times (14$ m s$^{-1})^2 = 1.2 \times 10^5$ J

5. Gain in E_k = loss in $E_{grav} = mg\Delta h$ so $\frac{1}{2} mv^2 = mg\Delta h$.

Cancelling m and rearranging:

$v^2 = 2g\Delta h = 2 \times 9.81$ m s^{-2} $\times 5.0$ m $= 98.1$ m^2 s^{-2}, so $v = 9.9$ m s^{-1}.

6 $\Delta W = mg\Delta h$ so $P = \dfrac{mg\Delta h}{\Delta t}$

$= 50$ kg $\times 9.81$ N kg^{-1} $\times \dfrac{2.0 \text{ m}}{2.5 \text{ s}} = 392$ W

Projectile motion

Page 11

1 The lander rises until its vertical component of velocity reaches zero: $v = 0$. The initial vertical component of velocity $u = 10$ m s^{-1} $\times \sin 50° = 7.7$ m s^{-1}. Taking upwards as positive, $a = -3.7$ m s^{-2}.

$v = u + at$ so time $t = \dfrac{(v - u)}{a} = \dfrac{(0 - 8.2 \text{ m s}^{-1})}{-3.7 \text{ m s}^{-2}} = 2.0$ s

The total time of the bounce is 2×2.0 s $= 4.0$ s (by symmetry, or use $v = u + at$ for the downward part of the vertical motion).

2 Horizontal component of velocity $u = 10$ m s^{-1} $\times \cos 50° = 6.4$ m s^{-1}, so horizontal distance $= 4.0$ s $\times 6.4$ m s^{-1} $= 26$ m.

3 $s = ut + \frac{1}{2}at^2$ (consider vertical motion)

$= 10$ m s^{-1} $\times \sin 50° \times 2.0$ s $+ \frac{1}{2} \times (-3.7 \text{ m s}^{-2}) \times (2.0 \text{ s})^2$

$= 15.3$ m $- 7.4$ m $= 7.9$ m

Take care with signs.

Electric circuits

Page 13

1 $\Delta Q = I\Delta t = 2$ C s^{-1} $\times 120$ s $= 240$ C

2 Resistance increases with pd. For example, when $V = 1$ V, $I = 1$ A and $R = 1$ Ω. When $V = 6$ V, $I = 2$ A and $R = 3$ Ω.

3 a $I = \dfrac{P}{V} = \dfrac{2.5 \times 10^3 \text{ J s}^{-1}}{230 \text{ J C}^{-1}} = 10.9$ C s^{-1}

b $R = \dfrac{V}{I} = \dfrac{230 \text{ V}}{10.9 \text{ A}} = 21.1$ Ω

c The kettle will still be connected to 230 V (the mains supply). $P = V^2/R$ so if R increases P will become smaller. The current will also decrease so the power will decrease.

Note that it is not valid to use $P = I^2R$ to argue that an increase in R leads to an increase in P, because I changes as well as R.

4 Power input $P = VI = 1.10$ V $\times 0.95$ A $= 1.045$ W.

Useful power output $= \dfrac{0.470 \text{ J}}{2.6 \text{ s}} = 0.180$ W.

Efficiency $= \dfrac{0.180 \text{ W}}{1.045 \text{ W}} = 0.17 = 17\%$.

or Energy input $= VIt = 1.10$ V $\times 0.95$ A $\times 2.6$ s $= 2.72$ J.

Efficiency $= \dfrac{0.470 \text{ J}}{2.72 \text{ J}} = 0.17 = 17\%$.

Combining resistors

Page 14

1 a $\dfrac{1}{R} = \dfrac{1}{1 \text{ Ω}} + \dfrac{1}{2 \text{ Ω}} + \dfrac{1}{3 \text{ Ω}} = 1$ Ω^{-1} $+ 0.5$ Ω^{-1} $+ 0.33$ Ω^{-1} $= 1.83$ Ω^{-1}

$R = \dfrac{1}{1.83 \text{ Ω}^{-1}} = 0.55$ Ω

b Start with the resistors in parallel:

$\dfrac{1}{R} = \dfrac{1}{1 \text{ Ω}} + \dfrac{1}{3 \text{ Ω}} = 1$ Ω^{-1} $+ 0.33$ Ω^{-1} $= 1.33$ Ω^{-1}

$R = \dfrac{1}{1.33 \text{ Ω}^{-1}} = 0.75$ Ω

Now we have 0.75 Ω in series with 4 Ω so total $R = 0.75$ Ω $+ 4$ Ω $= 4.75$ Ω.

c Start with the resistors in series which add up to 4 Ω, so we have a total of 4 Ω in parallel with 8 Ω.

$\dfrac{1}{R} = \dfrac{1}{4 \text{ Ω}} + \dfrac{1}{8 \text{ Ω}} = 0.25$ Ω^{-1} $+ 0.125$ Ω^{-1} $= 0.375$ Ω^{-1}

$R = \dfrac{1}{0.375 \text{ Ω}^{-1}} = 2.7$ Ω

Resistance and temperature

Page 15

1 See figures.

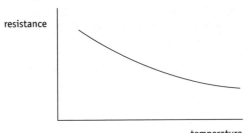

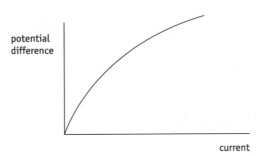

2 See figure. Notice that the graph uses a scale which is easy to plot and to read, and the axes are labelled with quantity/unit.

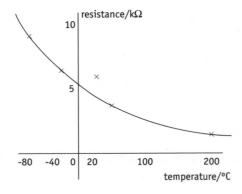

a About 3.2 kΩ (read from the graph).

b The point at 25 °C, because it lies a long way from the smooth curve through the other points.

c Resistance decreases as temperature increases. The component has a negative temperature coefficient.

Internal resistance

Page 17

1 a $\mathscr{E} = I(R + r)$, so $I = \dfrac{\mathscr{E}}{(R + r)} = \dfrac{1.5 \text{ V}}{4\ \Omega + 0.8\ \Omega} = \dfrac{1.5 \text{ V}}{4.8\ \Omega}$

$= 0.313$ A

b $V = IR = 0.313$ A $\times$ 4.0 Ω = 1.25 V

c $P = VI = 1.25$ V $\times$ 0.313 A = 0.39 W

d $I^2 r = (0.313 \text{ A})^2 \times 0.80\ \Omega = 0.08$ W

2 Output power $P = VI$. In a short circuit, I is large ($I = \mathscr{E}/R$) but $V = 0$ so $P = 0$. In an open circuit, the terminal pd has its greatest possible value ($V = \mathscr{E}$) but $I = 0$ so $P = 0$.

Heating and cooling

Page 19

1 $\Delta E = VIt = 12$ V $\times$ 2.2 A $\times$ 5 $\times$ 60 s = 7920 J

$c = \dfrac{\Delta E}{m \Delta \theta} = \dfrac{7920 \text{ J}}{1.0 \text{ kg} \times 8.6\ ^\circ C} = 921$ J kg^{-1} °C^{-1}

2 In 1 s, a mass m of water flows through the system. The energy supplied in this time is 200 J, which raises the water temperature by 8 °C.

$m = \dfrac{\Delta E}{c \Delta \theta} = \dfrac{200 \text{ J}}{(4.2 \times 10^3 \text{ J kg}^{-1} \text{ °C}^{-1} \times 8\ ^\circ C)} = 6 \times$

10^{-3} kg = 6 g. So the flow rate is 6 g s^{-1}.

Oscillations and waves

Page 21

1 Frequency $f = 10 \times 10^3$ Hz = 1×10^4 Hz

Period $T = \dfrac{1}{f} = \dfrac{1}{1 \times 10^4 \text{ Hz}} = 1 \times 10^{-4}$ s.

Wavelength $\lambda = \dfrac{v}{f} = \dfrac{338 \text{ m s}^{-1}}{1 \times 10^4 \text{ Hz}} = 3.38 \times 10^{-2}$ m.

2 Wavelength $\lambda = \dfrac{v}{f} = \dfrac{1.6 \text{ m s}^{-1}}{2.0 \text{ Hz}} = 0.8$ m.

Period $T = \dfrac{1}{f} = \dfrac{1}{2.0 \text{ Hz}} = 0.5$ s (see figure).

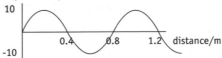

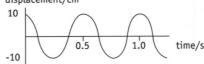

Superposition

Page 23

1 Destructive superposition occurs, producing complete cancellation (see figure).

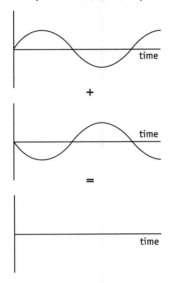

2 At D, the *path difference* is equal to exactly 0.5 wavelengths, so waves arrive *in antiphase*. A crest from A always arrives at the same time as a trough from B, and a trough from A with a crest from B. Destructive *superposition* takes place.

3 The sources are not *coherent*, i.e. the *phase* relationship between the two sets of waves keeps changing. At any one instant there will be places where the overlapping waves arrive in phase and others where they arrive in antiphase, but a few nanoseconds later the phase relationship will have changed so the positions of constructive and destructive superposition will be different.

Standing waves

Page 25

1 Wavelength $\lambda = 2 \times 6$ cm $= 0.12$ m.

$v = f\lambda = 2450 \times 10^6$ Hz $\times 0.12$ m $= 2.9 \times 10^8$ m s^{-1}

2 The pitch falls. Increasing μ reduces the wave speed, so for the *same wavelength* the frequency must be lower.

3 $\dfrac{\lambda}{2} = 30$ cm so $\lambda = 60$ cm $= 0.60$ m

$f = \dfrac{v}{\lambda} = \dfrac{200 \text{ m s}^{-1}}{0.60 \text{ m}} = 333$ Hz

4 Now $\lambda = 4 \times 2.0$ m $= 8.0$ m and $f = \dfrac{330 \text{ m s}^{-1}}{8.0 \text{ m}} = 41.3$ Hz.

5 The note produced by the 6 cm pipe has half the wavelength and hence twice the frequency of that produced by the 12 cm pipe.

6 There is a node at one end and an antinode at the other. The figure shows one possibility. In this example,

length of tube $= \dfrac{3}{4} \times$ wavelength

so $\lambda = \dfrac{4l}{3}$ where l is the length of the tube.

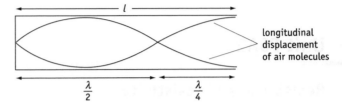

Lenses

Page 27

1 One lens has twice the focal length of the other, hence half the power.

$f = 20$ cm $= 0.20$ m, $P = \dfrac{1}{0.20 \text{ m}} = 5.0$ D

$f = 40$ cm $= 0.40$ m, $P = \dfrac{1}{0.40 \text{ m}} = 2.5$ D

Remember to express the focal length in metres.

Photons and spectra

Page 29

1 See the table below.

Comparing values

colour	typical wavelength/ nm	frequency/Hz	photon energy/J
ultraviolet	300	1.00×10^{15}	6.63×10^{-19}
blue	410	7.32×10^{14}	4.85×10^{-19}
red	660	4.55×10^{14}	3.02×10^{-19}
infrared	800	3.75×10^{14}	2.49×10^{-19}

2 a $E = \dfrac{hc}{\lambda}$

$= \dfrac{6.63 \times 10^{-34} \text{ J s} \times 3.00 \times 10^8 \text{ m s}^{-1}}{670 \times 10^{-9} \text{ m}}$

$= 2.96 \times 10^{-19}$ J

b Energy emitted in 1 second $= 5 \times 10^{-3}$ J.

No. of photons $= \dfrac{5 \times 10^{-3} \text{ J}}{2.96 \times 10^{-19} \text{ J}} = 1.69 \times 10^{16}$

photons per second.

3 There are three possible photon energies, frequencies and wavelengths:

$E_3 - E_1 = 0.309 \times 10^{-18}$ J

$f = \dfrac{E_3 - E_1}{h} = 4.66 \times 10^{14}$ Hz

$\lambda = \dfrac{c}{f} = \dfrac{3.00 \times 10^8 \text{ m s}^{-1}}{4.66 \times 10^{14} \text{ Hz}} = 6.44 \times 10^{-7}$ m = 644 nm.

$E_2 - E_1 = 0.234 \times 10^{-18}$ J

$f = \dfrac{E_2 - E_1}{h} = 3.53 \times 10^{14}$ Hz

$\lambda = \dfrac{c}{f} = \dfrac{3.00 \times 10^8 \text{ m s}^{-1}}{3.53 \times 10^{14} \text{ Hz}} = 8.50 \times 10^{-7}$ m = 850 nm.

$E_3 - E_2 = 0.075 \times 10^{-18}$ J

$f = \dfrac{E_3 - E_2}{h} = 1.13 \times 10^{14}$ Hz

$\lambda = \dfrac{c}{f} = \dfrac{3.00 \times 10^8 \text{ m s}^{-1}}{1.13 \times 10^{14} \text{ Hz}} = 2.65 \times 10^{-6}$ m = 2650 nm.

Unit PSA2

Resistance and resistivity

Page 36

1 $\rho = \dfrac{RA}{l}$

2 $r = 2.5 \times 10^{-3}$ m so $A = \pi \times (2.5 \times 10^{-3} \text{ m})^2$

$l = 10 \times 10^{-2}$ m = 0.1 m

$\rho = \dfrac{RA}{l} = 1.0 \times 10^{15} \ \Omega \times \pi \times (2.5 \times 10^{-3} \text{ m})^2 / 0.1 \text{ m} = $

$2.0 \times 10^{11} \ \Omega$ m

3 $\log_{10} \rho_{\text{carbon}} = \log_{10} (1.6 \times 10^{-5}) = -4.8$

Potential dividers

Page 39

1 4 V. (It has $\frac{1}{3}$ the total resistance and hence $\frac{1}{3}$ of the total pd.)

2 The pd between B and C *decreases* because the resistance between B and C becomes a smaller fraction of the total between A and C.

3 See figure. The pd rises all along the wire, reaching V (the supply pd). It rises rapidly with length along the thinner sections (high resistance per unit length) and more slowly along the thicker sections (low resistance per unit length). The right-hand part of the graph resembles the figure for the non-uniform wire on page 37.

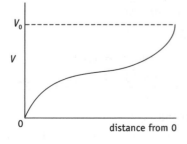

Nuclear radiation

Page 41

1 a all of α, β and γ

b all of α, β and γ

c α only

d γ only

e β only (α cannot penetrate, γ causes little ionisation)

Photoelectric effect

Page 45

1 $f_0 = \dfrac{\phi}{h} = \dfrac{4.00 \times 10^{-19} \text{ J}}{6.63 \times 10^{-34} \text{ J s}} = 6.03 \times 10^{14}$ Hz

2 $E_{k\,\text{max}} = hf - \phi$

$= 6.63 \times 10^{-34} \text{ J s} \times 7.06 \times 10^{14} \text{ Hz} -$

$4.00 \times 10^{-19} \text{ J}$

$= 6.81 \times 10^{-20} \text{ J}$

3 The frequency is less than the threshold frequency for barium, so the photon energy is less than the work function. Absorbing a photon of this energy does not give an electron enough energy to escape for the metal, so this red light does not cause the emission of any photoelectrons from barium; it just heats the barium very slightly.

4 **a** A, **b** B, **c** B, **d** A

Using straight-line graphs

Page 47

1 y intercept $c = -hf_0$

Fluid flow

Page 51

1 **a** turbulent flow; **b** streamlined or laminar flow

2 The warm syrup will flow more quickly than the cold syrup, because its *viscosity* becomes less as temperature rises.

3 **a** C, **b** A, **c** D, **d** B, **e** C, **f** B

4 The arrow should be the same length as the 'weight' arrow and point upwards.

5 If the fluid's density is much less than that of the object, then the upthrust is much smaller than the object's weight and can be ignored in comparison.

6 $6\pi\eta r v_T = mg - U = \dfrac{4\pi r^3 \rho_s g}{3} - \dfrac{4\pi r^3 \rho_f g}{3}$

   so $v_T = \dfrac{2r^2 g(\rho_s - \rho_f)}{9\eta}$

Refraction

Page 53

1 $_g\mu_w = \dfrac{v_g}{v_w} = \dfrac{1}{(v_w / v_g)} = \dfrac{1}{_w\mu_g} = \dfrac{1}{1.15} = 0.87$

2 The light is refracted into the denser material making an angle C with the normal. The diagram looks like diagram (b) on page 53 with the reflected ray removed and the arrows reversed.

3 Some light will always be reflected back into the water in such a way that the angle of reflection (between reflected ray and normal) is equal to the angle of incidence (between incident ray and normal). Depending on the angle of incidence, some light may also be refracted out into the air. The critical angle C is the largest angle of incidence which allows this to happen. $\sin C = 1/_a\mu_w$ where $_a\mu_w$ is the refractive index from air to water. If the angle of incidence is greater than C, there is total internal reflection: all light is reflected at the interface and none emerges into the air.

Pulse echo techniques

Page 55

1 Such a technique uses a short pulse (short burst) of waves. At any interface between two different materials, there is partial *reflection*; this happens both at the 'front' and 'back' of the object. The time between the pulse being sent out and the reception of the first reflected pulse indicates the distance between the transmitter/receiver and the front of the object (2 × distance = wave speed × time interval). The time interval between the first and second reflected pulse similarly indicates the front-to-back distance. If the object is moving, the frequency of the waves is *Doppler shifted* – if the object is moving away, the frequency of the waves in the received pulse is lower than that of the original pulse, and if the object is approaching, the frequency is higher. The greater the velocity towards/away from the receiver, the greater the Doppler shift.

Lenses

Page 57

1 $f = -50$ cm, $v = -25$ cm

   $\dfrac{1}{u} = \dfrac{1}{f} - \dfrac{1}{v} = -\dfrac{1}{50 \text{ cm}} - \left(-\dfrac{1}{25 \text{ cm}}\right) =$

   $-0.02 \text{ cm}^{-1} + 0.04 \text{ cm}^{-1} = +0.02 \text{ cm}^{-1}$

   $u = \dfrac{1}{0.02 \text{ cm}^{-1}} = 50$ cm

Polarisation

Page 59

1 With plain water in the cell, adjust the moveable filter to give maximum extinction (darkness). Note its angular position θ_0.

   For each following measurement, make sure that the cell is filled to the same depth.

   For each solution of known concentration, c, record the angular setting θ_c that gives maximum extinction and calculate the rotation angle $R_c = \theta_c - \theta_0$. Repeat with the solution of unknown concentration, x, to find θ_x and hence R_x.

   Plot a graph of R_c against c for all the solutions of known concentration. Use the value of R_x to read x from the graph.

Properties of materials

Page 60

1 (a) elastic deformation; (b) plastic deformation

2 Here are just two examples. Glass is *hard* (it does not dent) but not *tough* (it breaks under sudden impact, e.g. when dropped). Leather is *tough* (it is difficult to cut or tear) but not *hard* (it is quite easy to dent or scratch its surface).

Energy in stretching a sample

Page 61

1 Between B and C there are about 165 squares each representing 2.0×10^{-2} J so the work done in stretching from B to C is about $165 \times 2.0 \times 10^{-2}$ J = 3.3 J.

   Adding the work done in stretching from 0 to B, the total work done in breaking the wire is about 4.6 J.

Materials under stress

Page 65

1 a Stress: N m^{-2} (also written N/m^2) or Pa. 1 N m^{-2} = 1 Pa.

  b Strain: no units. It is a ratio of two lengths so the units cancel.

2 r = 1.5 mm = 1.5×10^{-3} m. $A = \pi \times (1.5 \times 10^{-3}$ m$)^2$

$F = \sigma A = 3.5 \times 10^8$ Pa $\times \pi \times (1.5 \times 10^{-3}$ m$)^2$ = 2.5×10^3 N = 2.5 kN

3 ε = 0.25% = 0.0025. $\Delta x = \varepsilon x$ = 0.0025 $\times$ 1.2 m = 0.0030 m = 3.0 mm

4 The brittle material is (a).

5 $E = \dfrac{Fx}{A\Delta x}$

6 ε = 0.1% = 0.1×10^{-2} = 1×10^{-3}; σ = 70×10^6 Pa

$E = \dfrac{70 \times 10^6 \text{ Pa}}{1 \times 10^{-3}}$ = 7×10^{10} Pa (= 70 GPa)

X-rays and diffraction

Page 66

1 The size and separation of the atoms in the crystal must be comparable to the wavelength of the X-rays, in order to produce noticeable diffraction. The visible light has a much longer wavelength so is not diffracted.

Polymers and electron diffraction

Page 67

1 In some circumstances electrons can behave like waves, with a *wavelength* that depends on their speed. If these waves meet atoms whose size and separation is comparable to their wavelength they undergo noticeable *diffraction*. They are readily affected by light atoms, such as carbon, which is the basis of many polymers. The pattern of the diffracted beams indicates the arrangement of atoms in the material: a regular arrangement gives rise to a few strong beams.

Answers to practice exam questions

Unit PSA1

1 Uniform acceleration from 0 s to 40 s ✓

$$a = \frac{\Delta v}{\Delta t} = \frac{20 \text{ m s}^{-1}}{40 \text{ s}} = 0.5 \text{ m s}^{-2}$$ ✓

From slope of graph at $t = 80$ s ✓

$$a = \frac{\Delta v}{\Delta t} = \frac{20 \text{ m s}^{-1}}{130 \text{ s}} = 0.15 \text{ m s}^{-2}$$ ✓

A range of answers would be allowed, e.g. 0.12–0.18 m s^{-2}.

At $t = 140$ s $a = 0$ m s^{-2} ✓

Force that produced uniform acceleration, $F = ma = 200\ 000 \text{ kg} \times 0.5 \text{ m s}^{-1} =$ 100 000 N ✓

To find distance, use area under section of graph:

distance $= \frac{1}{2} \times 20 \text{ m s}^{-1} \times 40 \text{ s} = 400$ m ✓✓

2 Weight W $= mg$ ✓

                        $= (70 \text{ kg} + 20 \text{ kg}) \times 9.81 \text{ N kg}^{-1} = 883$ N ✓

Vertical components $= 200 \text{ N} \cos 30° + 550 \text{ N} \cos 14°$ ✓

                        $= 173 \text{ N} + 534 \text{ N} = 707$ N ✓

                        which is close to 700 N

'In equilibrium' means no unbalanced force is acting ✓

Total vertical force is zero so $F \sin 37° + 707 \text{ N} = W = 883$ N ✓

so $F \sin 37° = 883 \text{ N} - 707 \text{ N} = 176$ N

$$F = \frac{176 \text{ N}}{\sin 37°} = 292 \text{ N}$$ ✓

Up to two marks for any sensible relevant statement, e.g.: ✓✓
- free foot accelerates upwards, which needs an upward force
- overall, climber must now experience an upward force which could arise from an increase in the force on his other foot
- climber pushes downward on rock, and reaction force from rock is upwards.

Note: London Qualifications Ltd (Edexcel) accepts no responsibility whatsoever for the accuracy or method of working in the answers given.

3 Consider vertical motion: $s = ut + \frac{1}{2}at^2$, with $u = 0$ ✓

$$t^2 = \frac{2s}{a} = \frac{2 \times 2.50 \text{ m}}{9.81 \text{ m s}^{-2}} = 0.510 \text{ s}^2, \text{ so } t = 0.714 \text{ s}$$ ✓

Ball travels horizontally through 21.0 m in 0.714 s, so $v = \frac{s}{t}$ ✓

$$v = \frac{21.0 \text{ m}}{0.714 \text{ s}} = 29.4 \text{ m s}^{-1}$$ ✓

Vertical component of velocity after 0.714 s:

either $\quad v = u + at = 9.81 \text{ m s}^{-2} \times 0.714 \text{ s} = 7.0 \text{ m s}^{-1}$ ✓

or $\quad v^2 = u^2 + 2as = 2 \times 9.81 \text{ m s}^{-2} \times 2.50 \text{ m} = 49 \text{ m}^2 \text{ s}^{-2} \text{ so } v = 7.0 \text{ m s}^{-1}$

Horizontal component is still 29.4 m s^{-1} ✓

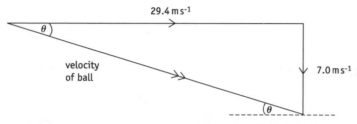

Diagram showing velocity at angle θ to the horizontal ✓

either use $\tan \theta = \dfrac{7.0}{29.4}$ so $\theta = 13.4°$ ✓✓

or measure θ from a scale drawing

Marks are given for suitable diagrams even if you are not asked to draw one.

One mark for any correct relevant statement, e.g.: ✓

Air resistance would reduce the speed, and the horizontal component would be affected more than the vertical component because it is greater. This would increase the angle θ.

In questions such as this you are expected to use your knowledge of physics to suggest a reasonable answer.

4 Wh is a unit of power × time so is a unit of energy ✓

m^3 is a unit of volume ✓

    (i) $\quad P = IV$ ✓

$$I = \frac{P}{V} = \frac{90 \text{ W}}{6.0 \text{ V}} = 15 \text{ A}$$ ✓

    (ii) $\quad \mathscr{E} = V + Ir$ ✓

$$= 6.0 \text{ V} + 15 \text{ A} \times 0.020 \text{ } \Omega = 6.3 \text{ V}$$ ✓

(iii) $P = I^2 r = (15 \text{ A})^2 \times 0.020 \ \Omega = 4.5 \text{ W}$ ✓

(iv) This power heats the battery. ✓

(v) Efficiency = useful output power/total power

$$= \frac{90 \text{ W}}{90 \text{ W} + 4.5 \text{ W}} = 0.952 = 95\%$$ ✓

Use energy conservation to deduce that the total power must be the useful power plus the power wasted in heating the internal resistance.

Output power = 90 W so input power = 900 W ✓

If the panels collect 1.4 kW per m^2 (1400 W per m^2), then

input power = 1400 W m^{-2} × area

so area $= \dfrac{900 \text{ W}}{1400 \text{ W m}^{-2}} = 0.64 \text{ m}^2$ ✓

A greater area is needed if the sunlight does not meet the surface at right angles. ✓

5 Electrical energy supplied by the heater ✓

is used to heat the water. ✓

Beware of giving vague answers to questions such as this which draw on GCSE work. Two marks generally require two precise statements.

$VIt = mc\Delta\theta$ or $Pt = mc\Delta\theta$ where P = power ✓

To gain this mark you need to relate two equations given at the back of the paper.

Dealing with a time interval of 1 minute:

$$\Delta\theta = \frac{Pt}{mc} = \frac{10.8 \times 10^3 \text{ W} \times 60 \text{ s}}{16 \text{ kg} \times 4200 \text{ J kg}^{-1}{}^{\circ}\text{C}^{-1}}$$ ✓

$$= 9.6 \ {}^{\circ}\text{C}$$ ✓

So final temperature = 15 °C + 9.6 °C = 24.6 °C ✓

In 'show that ...' questions, do the complete calculation and compare your answer with the one given.

$\Delta\theta = 20 \ {}^{\circ}\text{C}$ ✓

Mass flowing in 1 minute:

$$m = \frac{Pt}{c\Delta\theta} = \frac{10.8 \times 10^3 \text{ W} \times 60 \text{ s}}{4200 \text{ J kg}^{-1}{}^{\circ}\text{C}^{-1} \times 20 \ {}^{\circ}\text{C}} = 7.7 \text{ kg}$$

so the flow rate is 7.7 kg min^{-1} ✓

(Or use an interval of $t = 1$ s and find the flow rate is 0.13 kg s^{-1}.)

The metal element is cold so its resistance will be lower and there will be a greater current when connected to the mains voltage. ✓

6 The vibrating string causes compressions and rarefactions in the air. ✓

These travel through the air as longitudinal vibrations, i.e. as a sound wave. ✓

A frequency of 10 MHz is too high to be heard. ✓

Just saying 'cannot be heard' would not gain a mark as that just repeats the question. You need to give a reason.

$\lambda = 2 \times$ length of string $= 2 \times 10 \times 10^{-6}$ m $= 2 \times 10^{-5}$ m ✓

Assumption: there is a single antinode in the middle. ✓

Speed $v = f\lambda = 10 \times 10^{6}$ Hz $\times 2 \times 10^{-5}$ m $= 200$ m s^{-1} ✓✓

$v = \sqrt{\dfrac{T}{\mu}}$ so $v^2 = \dfrac{T}{\mu}$ and $T = \mu v^2$ ✓

$T = (200 \text{ m s}^{-1})^2 \times 4 \times 10^{-12}$ kg m$^{-1} = 1.6 \times 10^{-7}$ N ✓

7 Line spectra contain only certain distinct colours ✓

i.e. certain distinct frequencies and wavelengths ✓

One mark for each correct point, up to a maximum of three, e.g.: ✓✓✓
- light can be described in terms of photons
- each colour (or frequency) corresponds to a certain photon energy
- photons are emitted (or absorbed) when electrons in atoms lose (or gain) energy
- the photon energies correspond to energy transitions within atoms
- only a few distinct transitions occur so the energy of electrons in atoms must be limited to certain distinct values.

8

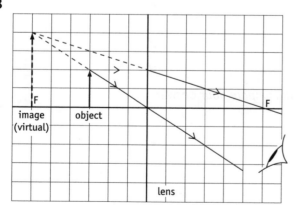

The diagram should show:
- two rays correctly drawn ✓✓
- rays traced back to produced a virtual image. ✓

Image distance = 30 cm ✓

It is difficult to measure the distance precisely from the diagram so examiners allow a range of values, e.g. 28–32 cm.

$$\text{Magnification} = \frac{20 \text{ cm}}{10 \text{ cm}} = 2 \qquad \checkmark\checkmark$$

Notice that magnification is a ratio of two lengths and so has no units.

Unit PSA2

1 The wire gets longer and/or thinner, i.e. l increases, A decreases   ✓

$R = \dfrac{\rho l}{A}$ so either of these changes will *increase* the resistance   ✓

A long wire is contained in a small area/the extension is multiplied because each section is stretched   ✓

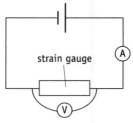

Power supply with gauge in series with ammeter   ✓

and in parallel with voltmeter   ✓

or

Diagram with multimeter connected to gauge

Drawing a multimeter and power supply would score only one mark.

$R = \dfrac{\rho l}{A}$ ✓

$= \dfrac{4.9 \times 10^{-7}\,\Omega\ \text{m} \times 0.2\ \text{m}}{\pi \times (1 \times 10^{-4}\ \text{m})^2}$ ✓

$= 3.1\ \Omega$ ✓

2 $E = hf = 6.63 \times 10^{-34}\ \text{J s} \times 6.2 \times 10^{14}\ \text{Hz} = 4.1 \times 10^{-19}\ \text{J}$ ✓

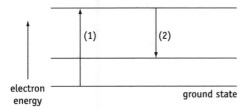

Arrow going *upwards* from ground state.   ✓

Second arrow going *down* to intermediate level   ✓

When blue light is absorbed, electron is excited to a higher energy level.   ✓

Electron loses some of its additional energy and falls to an intermediate level. ✓

The frequency, and hence the colour, depends on the difference *between two energy levels.*

In liquids, molecules are close together so electrons occupy energy bands rather than single levels ✓

so there is a range of possible energy transitions and hence a range of possible frequencies that can be absorbed/emitted ✓

This part expects a sensible suggestion based on knowledge of energy bands in solids.

3 hf is the energy of the in-coming photon ✓

ϕ is the work function of the metal ✓

which is the minimum energy needed to release an electron ✓

joules (J) ✓

Two marks for any two of these points: ✓✓
- for a given photon energy hf, electrons are emitted with a range of energies
- some electrons transfer energy to the metal on their way to the surface
- 'max' refers to the kinetic energy of electrons that have lost no energy while leaving the metal.

4 Viscous drag: force that opposes motion through a fluid ✓

Laminar flow: continuous streamlines/no turbulence ✓

This answer would be enhanced by a diagram based on the figure on page 51.

Terminal velocity: constant (non-zero) velocity reached when there is no net force acting ✓✓

Diagram showing:
- weight: downward arrow
- drag: upward arrow
- upthrust: upward arrow. ✓

Weight $W = mg$, $m = \rho V$

$$W = \frac{4\pi r^3 \sigma g}{3}$$ ✓

Upthrust: due to oil displaced by sphere ✓

At terminal velocity net force = 0 so $W = F + U$, $F = W - U$ ✓

$$6\pi \eta r v = \frac{4\pi r^3 \rho g}{3} - \frac{4\pi r^3 \sigma g}{3}$$ ✓

$$= \frac{4\pi r^3 (\rho - \sigma) g}{3}$$

cancelling π and dividing by $6rv$:

$$\eta = \frac{4r^3 (\rho - \sigma) g}{3 \times 6rv} = \frac{2r^2 (\rho - \sigma) g}{9v}$$ ✓

Viscosity varies with temperature ✓

and the test must model the real use. ✓

5 Light that meets the juice–glass boundary at less than the critical angle ✓

is refracted into the juice so little light reaches the scale ✓

Be careful to word your answer clearly and precisely using appropriate technical terms. A vague answer such as 'light is refracted' would gain no marks.

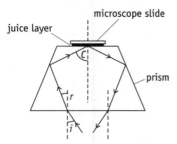

Angle *C* between ray and normal at glass–juice interface ✓

Angle *i* between incident ray and normal at glass–air interface ✓

Angle *r* between refracted ray and normal at glass–air interface ✓

- *In this example light does not refract into the juice, so look for a surface where refraction does occur.*
- *Remember to draw the normals to the surfaces.*
- *Use a ruler and a sharp pencil for ray diagrams.*

Critical angle: the *largest* incident angle that allows refraction into a less dense material

or the *smallest* incident angle that gives rise to total internal reflection

or the incident angle where the refracted angle in the more dense material is 90° ✓✓

For both marks, you need to be clear that the angle is the largest (or smallest) that gives rise to refraction (or total internal reflection).

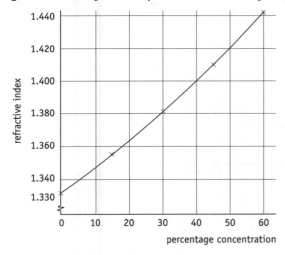

Sensible choice of scale on *y*-axis ✓

Sensible choice of scale on *x*-axis ✓

Choose a scale that is easy to plot and read, and that uses at least half the length or width of the paper. Make sure the scale has equal values at equal intervals! In this case it is sensible not to start the y-axis at zero.

Points correctly plotted   ✓

Best-fit curve drawn   ✓

- *Use a sharp pencil for drawing graphs.*
- *In this example the best-fit line is a curve. The measurements are very precise and are not consistent with a straight line.*

From the graph: refractive index = 1.400   ✓

- *Answers within 0.002 of this answer would gain a mark.*
- *The data have four significant figures, and the answer read from the graph has at least three figures. Less precise answers gain no marks.*

6 Time   ✓

Reflected pulses   ✓

from both boundaries between head and surrounding fluid

or   from near and far side of head.   ✓

Time t between peaks found from trace.   ✓

Knowing speed v of ultrasound in head   ✓

calculate width of head $= \dfrac{vt}{2}$ ✓

Use symbols and equations to make the explanation precise and compact.

Doppler shift: the change in frequency of received waves   ✓

caused by relative motion of source/reflector and observer   ✓

7 Diverging (because it forms a virtual image of a distant object)   ✓

Focal length $f = -2.0$ m (image distance for distant object)   ✓

To get the mark, the sign must be correct.

Power $= \dfrac{1}{f} = -0.5$ D   ✓

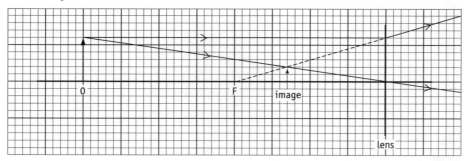

ray parallel to axis is refracted as if coming from F   ✓

ray through lens centre is undeviated   ✓

virtual image at point where both rays appear to originate   ✓

- *Ray diagrams are discussed in PSA1.*
- *Use a ruler and a sharp pencil for ray diagrams.*

$P = P_1 + P_2 = -0.5\text{ D} + 0.20\text{ D} = -0.3\text{ D}$ ✓

His sight has improved as he does not need such a strong lens as before.   ✓

To get a mark you need to give an explanation as well as stating that his sight has improved.

8   Plane polarised: vibrations (of electric field) in one plane only   Ordinary light: vibrations in all planes   ✓

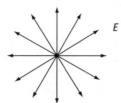

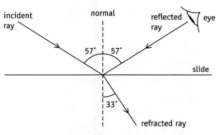

Incident, reflected and refracted rays, with angles marked   ✓✓✓

- *Don't forget the eye that the question asked for!*
- *Remember to draw arrows on the rays.*

Light changes intensity   ✓

from dim to bright twice for each complete turn.   ✓

A diagram similar to the figure on page 58 would enhance this answer, but be careful – here there is just one filter as the light is already polarised by the slide.

The filter only allows light through that vibrates in one plane.   ✓

When the filter is in line with this plane, bright light is seen. When the filter is at 90° to this plane, little or no light is seen.   ✓

$\mu = \dfrac{\sin i}{\sin r} = \dfrac{\sin 57°}{\sin 33°} = 1.54$ ✓

9

property	explanation	example	
brittle	*no plastic deformation before breaking*	glass	✓
malleable	*can be hammered into a new permanent shape*	lead	✓✓
stiff	large stress produces only small strain	*steel*	✓
ductile	*can be drawn into wires*	copper	✓

- *Examples of correct answers are in italic. Other correct alternatives would also gain full marks.*
- *Be careful to distinguish between ductile and malleable.*

Index